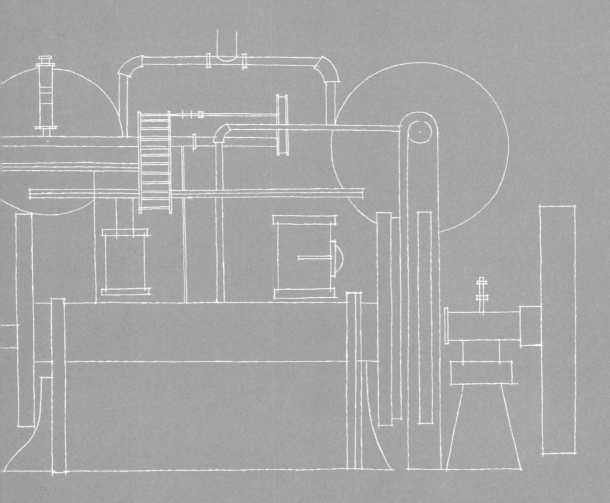

AMERICAN BUREAU OF SHIPPING

*American Bureau
of Shipping Building
New York City*

American
Bureau
of Shipping

ONE HUNDREDTH
ANNIVERSARY

1862 ★ 1962

NEW YORK · 1962

Table of Contents

"They that go down to the sea in ships,
That do business in great waters;
These see the works of the Lord,
And his wonders in the deep."

DAVID, 107TH PSALM

TO PROTECT SUCH MEN AND TO
PRESERVE THE PROPERTY IN THEIR CARE
WAS THE PRIMARY INCENTIVE FOR
THE ORGANIZATION,
THE HISTORICAL RECORD OF WHICH
IS HEREIN SET FORTH

Foreword

This book has been prepared, and is presented, as a memento of the 100th anniversary of the founding of the American Bureau of Shipping. Originally conceived as the American Shipmasters' Association, the organization was incorporated on April 22, 1862, and was established on a working basis by July 23 of the same year.

Much has already been written on the early history and activities of the Bureau in its first 75 years of existence as a national Classification Society. Originating in the Clipper Ship Era of the country, the Bureau early experienced a decline in activity as the sailing ship gradually faded out as a factor in world trade. As a result, it had no appreciable growth for about fifty years. The start of World War One in Europe in 1914, however, provided a stimulus to the ship operating and shipbuilding industries in the United States and the fortunes of the Bureau improved accordingly. In the years between the two great Wars, the Bureau became firmly entrenched as the National Classification Society of the United States.

The last 25 years have been marked by some of the most important changes and accomplishments in the 100 year history of the American Bureau of Shipping. It was during this period that the organization was transformed into an International Classification Society. Since the celebration of the 75th Anniversary in 1937 of the founding of the Bureau, World War II has been fought and the Bureau has been vitally involved in the great merchant shipbuilding program which developed. With the end of the war came the postwar expansion, which involved the opening of exclusive offices in the principal seaports of the world. Some of the outstanding and important technical developments in the design, building and powering of merchant vessels have occurred in this postwar era, and in these developments the Bureau has been intimately concerned. The establishment of new Head-quarters in the present building at 45 Broad Street, New York, also occurred in this period.

Origin and Growth

In this part an attempt has been made to present to the reader in very brief form the story of the American Bureau of Shipping, from the granting of the original charter to the American Shipmasters' Association on April 22, 1862, through the change in chartered title to the American Bureau of Shipping granted on September 22, 1898, and thence through the reorganization in 1916 up to the celebration of the Bureau's One Hundredth Anniversary on April 22, 1962. During this period the Bureau has attained the position of one of the foremost Ship Classification Societies in the world.

1

General History

The American Shipmasters' Association was organized in the year 1861, although preparatory meetings had been held a year earlier. John D. Jones, President of the Atlantic Mutual Insurance Company, presented a plan of organization.

Participating in this historic undertaking were the presidents and vice presidents of the following marine insurance companies, viz.: Atlantic Mutual, Sun Mutual, Mercantile Mutual, New York Mutual, Union Mutual, Oriental Mutual, Commercial Mutual, Pacific Mutual, and the Anchor Insurance Company. Later in the year, the Columbia Marine Insurance Company joined the original group. It is interesting to note that the Atlantic Mutual Insurance Company is the sole surviving member of this group of early marine insurance companies.

Stock was not issued to finance the organization of the Society, as the founders and participating companies each subscribed $700.00 and agreed, in addition, to accept assessment for any deficiency in operating expenses, in proportion to the premiums received by each company based upon its last published statement.

The original membership comprised marine underwriters, merchants, shipowners, shipmasters, shipbuilders, and persons prominently identified with maritime commerce in the United States of America, as well as persons officially connected with the United States Government and those in civil life prominent in the various branches of science appertaining to ship construction and operation.

It was deemed advisable by those familiar with the commerce of the United States, to encourage a higher degree of efficiency and character amongst the masters and officers of vessels. It seemed obviously desirable to encourage honest officers in the performance of their duties, and to exercise such available powers as would prevent the ignorant and dishonest minority from sacrificing lives and property through neglect of duty.

The Association engaged rooms 89 and 90 in the Merchants Exchange, Wall Street, New York City, for its headquarters, which were open to all officers holding commissions of the Association. Masters and mates of foreign vessels in port were also entitled to visit the rooms upon introduction by members of the Association.

Commissions were given to Masters and Mates for competency and service, after examination designed to establish their knowledge of nautical science and seamanship. These Commissions of Competency and Service were issued from 1862 up to the year 1900. The first application for a Certificate was received from Captain Isaiah Pratt in September, 1861. Although the United States Steamboat Inspection Service began licensing masters and mates in 1838, this service was later suspended and again renewed in 1852. This service was suspended a second time in 1860 and again renewed in 1870. For almost a decade the Association was the only organization in the United States which upheld a standard of efficiency among the sea-going officer personnel.

In 1862, the Association was authorized to employ competent examiners in nautical science, and to organize a system of examination not only in New York but in other cities.

Though meeting with considerable opposition at the outset of its career, the Association, nevertheless, continued in the course laid down by its founders until it eventually gained the unqualified approbation of all those interested in the vast commerce of our country, and of those desirous of seeing our shipping interests adequately developed.

The records show that in the first month, namely September, 1861, the American Shipmasters' Association received forty-one applications for Commissions from Masters and other Officers, and during the ensuing year, the large number of 1488 applications were received.

On the twenty-second day of April, 1862, the Association was duly incorporated by an Act of the Legislature of the State of New York, and divers powers and privileges were granted to it under the terms of its Charter.

As quoted in the Constitution and By-Laws, the objectives of the Association were to collect and disseminate information upon subjects of marine or commercial interest; to keep a record of and to encourage worthy and well qualified commanders, and other officers in the merchant service; to ascertain and certify the qualifications of such persons as shall apply to be recommended as such commanders or officers; to promote the security of life and property on the seas; to provide for shipowners, shipbuilders, underwriters, shippers and all interested in maritime commerce, a faithful and accurate Classification and Registry of mercantile shipping; and to aid and develop the Merchant Marine of the United States of America.

The new Association under the terms of its Charter was organized on July 23, 1862; Mr. John D. Jones, President of the Atlantic Mutual Insurance Company, was elected as the first President.

A proposal to institute a proper system of surveying, rating, and registering of vessels was adopted on February 25, 1867. The publication of the register of ratings and surveys, known as the *Record of American and Foreign Shipping,* was established in March, 1867, the early issues of the Register being published monthly in pamphlet form.

On April 2, 1868, the New York Board of Underwriters passed the following resolution:

"RESOLVED: That the Shipmasters' Association be requested to have a full Register of Vessels published as soon as possible; said Register to indicate, by a peculiar mark, all vessels which have not been specially surveyed by the Inspectors of the Association, but are described and rated from the best attainable authority, until special surveys can be had."

The first bound volume of the *Record of American and Foreign Shipping* was published in January, 1869. It contained a list of vessels, and gave general particulars as well as changes, repairs, and classification. There were two contemporary American publications, one entitled: *The American Lloyds Registry of American and Foreign Shipping,* stated as being published by Hartshorne & King; and the other, *The American Lloyds Universal Register of Shipping,* purporting as being published by Thomas D. Taylor. The first of these registers started its career in 1857 with Thomas D. Taylor, Richard T. Hartshorne, and John F. H. King, Inspectors for the Underwriters, as partners. It was not until 1867 that Thomas D. Taylor, who had separated from Hartshorne & King, published his first *American Lloyds Universal Register of Shipping.* On June 3, 1869, the Board of Underwriters indorsed and approved the new publication by the following resolutions:

"RESOLVED: That the Record of American and Foreign Shipping, published by the American Shipmasters' Association, is the only American publication of Survey and Classification of Vessels that now has the approval of this Board; and that we recommend it as deserving the confidence of those interested in shipping.

"RESOLVED: That the Committee on the American Shipmasters' Association be requested to act with that Association in devising means to maintain the merit and extend the usefulness of the work."

In accordance with the foregoing resolution, and as a result of collaboration between the inspectors of the various marine insurance companies and the Association, the preparation of *Rules for the Survey and Classing of Wooden Vessels,* Rules which had been in use in a tentative form in 1868 and 1869, were formally published in the 1870 edition of the "Record."

The first official *Rules for the Survey and Classing of Iron Vessels* of the American Shipmasters' Association were published in 1877.

On July 1, 1879, the American Shipmasters' Association published a booklet containing:

> Suggestions to Masters of Vessels.
> Rules of the Road at Sea.
> List of Persons who have applied for
>   Certificates of Competency and Service.

6

Post Office Address

Signature of L. W. Horton of Bristol, R. Island

This Certificate is granted on an Examination held at

New York October 22nd 1861

C. A. Sheldon — Examiner in Nautical Science

W. H. Story — Examiner in Seamanship

American Ship Masters' Association

NEW YORK

has been registered by this Association as

ANY APPROVED SHIPMASTER.

This Certificate is granted and received with the
understanding that it may be revoked at any
time under the Rules of this Association and
at its given either by notice to the holder or
by advertisement in the public papers.

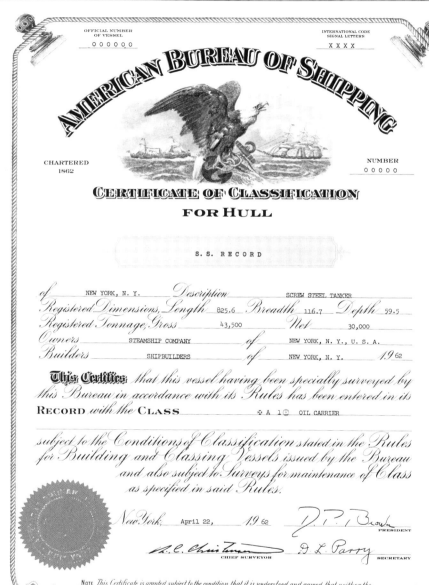

OFFICIAL NUMBER
OF VESSEL

O O O O O O

INTERNATIONAL CODE
SIGNAL LETTERS

X X X X

AMERICAN BUREAU OF SHIPPING

CHARTERED
1862

NUMBER

O O O O O

CERTIFICATE OF CLASSIFICATION
FOR HULL

S. S. R E C O R D

of   NEW YORK, N. Y.   *Description*   SCREW STEEL TANKER

Registered Dimensions, Length 825.6 *Breadth* 116.7 *Depth* 59.5

Registered Tonnage, Gross 43,500 *Net* 30,000

Owners   STEAMSHIP COMPANY   *of*   NEW YORK, N. Y., U. S. A.

Builders   SHIPBUILDERS   *of*   NEW YORK, N. Y.   19 62

This Certifies *that this vessel having been specially surveyed by this Bureau in accordance with its Rules has been entered in its* RECORD *with the* CLASS ⚓ A 1Ⓔ OIL CARRIER

subject to the Conditions of Classification stated in the Rules for Building and Classing Vessels issued by the Bureau and also subject to Surveys for maintenance of Class as specified in said Rules.

New York, April 22, 19 62   D. P. Brown
PRESIDENT

H. C. Christenson
CHIEF SURVEYOR

D. L. Parry
SECRETARY

It is interesting to note that there is a reference to a slogan, the "Seaman's Belief," as follows:

THE SEAMAN'S BELIEF
To be Said Daily and Acted on Always

"I understand L.L.L. to be the symbol or sign for three things which I must never neglect, and these things are:

LEAD   LOG   AND   LOOK-OUT

"I believe in the L E A D, as it warns me against dangers which the eye cannot see.

"I believe in the L O G, as it checks my distance run.

"I believe in the L O O K - O U T, as it warns me against dangers to be seen.

"The L E A D warns me against dangers invisible, the L O G warns me against false distances, and the L O O K - O U T warns me against dangers visible.

"And I earnestly resolve, and openly declare, that as I hope to sail my ship in safety on the ocean, as I wish to spare the lives of my fellow creatures at sea, and as I wish to go in safety all my days, so will I steadfastly practice that which I believe.

"And I hereby warn Seamen, and tell them that if they neglect any one of these three things, either the L E A D, the L O G, or the L O O K - O U T, they or their fellows will some day surely perish."

In accordance with a resolution adopted at a meeting of the Association held on September 25, 1884, the good-will and title to the *American Lloyds Universal Register* was purchased and combined with the "Record" on October 14, 1884.

In January, 1889, the *Rules for the Survey and Classing of Iron Vessels* having been revised, a copy was forwarded to the Hon. Benjamin F. Tracy, Secretary of the Navy, for the consideration and approval of the United States Navy Department.

A reply was received on July 12, 1889, as follows:

NAVY DEPARTMENT

Washington, July 11, 1889

"Sir:—

Referring to your communication of January 9th, 1889, submitting a copy of the rules adopted by the American Shipmasters' Association for the construction and classification of wooden and iron vessels, and requesting the approval of said rules by the Department, I have to inform you that the Department submitted your communication, together with a copy of the Rules referred to, to a board of officers for examination and report, and that the board, after an attentive consideration of the subject, made to the Department a report, a copy of which is, for your further information, enclosed herewith.

In this connection it is deemed proper to say that the Department is of the opinion that vessels built in accordance with the rules above referred to, modified as suggested in the report of said board, would be useful as auxiliary naval cruisers in time of war or in cases of emergency.

Very respectfully
B. F. TRACY
Secretary of the Navy"

Mr. W. R. T. Jones,
Secretary, American Shipmasters' Association,
No. 37 William Street,
New York, N.Y.

The first Advisory Council of Scientific and Practical Experts in the construction of Iron and Steel Vessels, known as the Advisory Council of Engineering and Marine Architects, was formed on December 2, 1892.

The Council was organized for the purpose of consultation on matters affecting the material, the designing, and the construction of iron and steel vessels and machinery, and for the further purpose of making suggestions for improving the "Rules" for construction of vessels.

In 1892, the Association issued *Rules for Steel Lake and River Vessels,* and in the following year the *Lakes Register of the Association Inland Lloyds* was compiled and published. However, this new register lacked the support of the underwriters and agents on the Great Lakes, and, in 1896, there was established by the Associated Lake Underwriters a *Great Lakes Register.* Although our book received very favorable commendation at the outset, contracts of insurance by underwriters on the Lakes were all made subject to class in the western publication *The Great Lakes Register.* Due to the loss of this most logical source of support, the publication of our Lakes book was eventually discontinued.

On September 26, 1898, the corporate name of the American Shipmasters' Association was changed to—American Bureau of Shipping—by authority from the Supreme Court of the State of New York.

On October 22, 1908, the American Bureau of Shipping purchased and absorbed the United States Standard Steamship Owners', Builders', and Underwriters' Association, Limited.

Following these activities, the affairs of the Bureau developed at a disappointingly slow pace, and in July, 1915, the president appointed a special team in an effort to learn the reason for the apparent reluctance on the part of shipowners and shipbuilders to engage the Bureau's services for the survey and classification of vessels. This team was directed to visit the various shipbuilders and owners to investigate and ascertain the cause or causes for the lack of support accorded. As a result of this investigation and a subsequent report submitted to the Bureau, a special meeting of the Board of Managers and Members of the American Bureau of Shipping was held on September 16, 1915, "for the purpose of dealing with the subject of reorganizing the Bureau and enlarging its usefulness." At this meeting there was appointed a special committee of the body assembled with full power to act in accordance with the purposes outlined in the call for the meeting.

After numerous meetings with shipowners, shipbuilders, and underwriters, as well as with representatives of Lloyd's Register of Shipping with which organization proposals to establish working agreements had been under consideration for some time previous, the Committee presented the following report at a deferred annual meeting of the Board of Managers on February 28, 1916.

"The Committee appointed to consider the question of the reorganization of the American Bureau of Shipping begs to report:

"That it has thoroughly canvassed the whole subject submitted, has held many meetings and conferences and there has been borne in upon the Committee from underwriters, shipowners, and shipbuilders and others interested a strong and insistent demand for an American Classification Association on broad lines of efficient progressive business and technical ability and administration—therefore the Committee recommend:

"That the Board of Managers be convened at once to take due action with respect to changes in the Constitution and By-Laws and to provide for the election of Mr. Stevenson Taylor as President of the American Bureau of Shipping at a satisfactory salary and direct the Committee to take the necessary steps with respect to finances and organization."

At this meeting, the following officers were elected:

STEVENSON TAYLOR . . . . President
ANTONIO C. PESSANO . . . . First Vice-President
FRANK GAIR MACOMBER . . . . Second Vice-President
JOHN W. CANTILLION . . . . Secretary-Treasurer

Funds were subscribed by various shipbuilders, underwriters, and owners for necessary expenses in connection with the reorganization. This money has long since been returned to the subscribers.

In May, 1916, the *Great Lakes Register,* established in 1896 for the registry and classification of vessels engaged in Great Lakes service, was acquired and continued under the title of the *Great Lakes Department of The American Bureau of Shipping.*

As all matters in connection with the construction of vessels for transoceanic service should, obviously, be considered of international importance, the Bureau reached an agreement in January, 1917, with the British Corporation for the Survey and Registry of Shipping. This agreement was motivated in the beginning by the urgent need of the Bureau to issue an entire new set of *Rules for the Construction of Steel Ships* in order that they be brought up to the standards and best modern practice.

This joint arrangement between the two societies was particularly satisfactory because it ensured harmonious action and an interchange of ideas advantageous to owners and builders on both sides of the Atlantic without interfering with the independence and national character of either society.

As the United States had not at that time enacted a Load Line Law, the arrangement immediately removed certain difficulties in regard to international recognition of load lines for American Bureau classed ships.

On March 1, 1917, an agreement for mutual cooperation and representation, similar to the British Corporation agreement, was made with the Registro Navale Italiano. On August 28, 1919, a like agreement was made with the Teikoku Kaiji Kyokai (Imperial Japanese Marine Corporation), which had been organized with the sanction of the Japanese Government.

In token of the respect and affection for the memory of Mr. Stevenson Taylor, the first president after the reorganization in 1916, and subsequently the first Chairman of the Board, who had passed away on the 19th day of May, 1926, the Bureau, in November, 1926, purchased the property located at 24 and 26 Old Slip, New York City, as a memorial. At a gathering of approximately one hundred and fifty—Managers, Members and employees of the Bureau—on Wednesday, October 27, 1927, the Stevenson Taylor Memorial Building was dedicated and officially turned over to the President by Mr. Walter Wood Parsons, Chairman of the Bureau's Building Committee, for use by the American Bureau of Shipping.

Following the reorganization in 1916, the opportunities for the growth and expansion of the Bureau's activities were greatly enhanced by the resurgence of shipbuilding in the United States resulting from the First World War. However, this period of rapidly expanding activity was soon followed by a period of depression in shipping and shipbuilding which lasted through the early 1930's.

In recognition of the rapidly dwindling position of the United States in world wide waterborne commerce and of the importance of an adequate merchant marine for defense purposes, the Government of the United States established the Maritime Commission, authorized to embark on a long range program of restoring the merchant fleet. Under this program, there were evolved the well-known standardized, modern, high speed cargo ships, desig-

24 Old Slip, New York

nated as the C-1, C-2 and C-3 types. These vessels became an important, integral part of the war shipbuilding program, which was soon to develop in the United States. The Bureau was consulted during the designing of these vessels, and its experienced technical staff was able to be of great assistance in the preliminary plan development. A total of 868 of these vessels, totaling 4,942,984 gross tons, were eventually built to the Bureau's requirements and Classed during the war years.

This early pre-war stimulation of the Bureau's business and activities was but the forerunner of the tremendous expansion which was to follow. With the declaration of war in Europe in September, 1939, the tempo of shipbuilding in the United States was stepped up. Accordingly, the Bureau's working force was expanded by increasing the technical staff and by stationing more surveyors at shipyards, steel mills and engine building plants.

Soon there was evolved, under an emergency program, the now famous Liberty cargo ship. New shipyards were created in all coastal areas of the country to construct these standard design vessels. This necessitated a further expansion of the Bureau, its staff, and facilities. Before the war terminated, a total of 2,710 Liberty type hulls, including the standard cargo ship and its derivations, such as tankers, colliers, Army tank carriers, and aircraft transports, were completed to Bureau Classification. These mass produced ships totaled 19,467,486 gross tons.

As the war effort was stepped up, it became necessary to replace the many oil tankers which were being sunk in the submarine warfare, and to construct additional tankship capacity to supply the spreading theatres of war. Shortly before the United States entered the war in December, 1941, there was evolved, with Bureau participation, the standard design of the T-2 oil tanker of 16,600 deadweight tons. Turbo-electric drive propelling machinery was selected for these vessels because of the then limited capacity for the production of reduction gears. A total of 525 T-2 turbo-electric drive tankers, aggregating 5,422,819 gross tons and 8,672,028

47 Beaver Street, New York

deadweight tons, were constructed to Bureau Classification requirements.

With the Liberty cargo ship emergency building program operating in high gear, it became evident that the efforts could be safely switched to a higher class of vessel with improved propelling machinery providing higher sea speeds than the simple triple expansion reciprocating steam engines utilized in the Liberty ships. New engine and gear building shops for the production of steam turbines were soon built, and a new design of a standard cargo ship produced. This design was known as the "Victory" cargo ship, a vessel of 7,600 gross tons and 10,600 deadweight tons. In this project the Bureau collaborated, by submitting designs by J. Lewis Luckenbach, President, and by arranging many conferences with the famous Vice Admiral Emory S. Land, USN, Chairman, and with Rear Admiral Howard L. Vickery, USN, Vice Chairman, of the Maritime Commission. A total of 531 Victory ships of several classes were ordered constructed to Bureau Classification, these aggregating 4,055,998 gross tons.

In all, some 5,171 seagoing vessels of many types, including troop transports, ore carriers, small and large cargo ships, and oil tankers, but excluding naval vessels, were produced in this war time shipbuilding program up to the end of 1945. These aggregated the huge total of 38,607,508 gross tons and 54,661,634 deadweight tons, equipped with propulsion machinery of 23,073,558 horsepower, all being built to Bureau Classification. In addition, there were many special types of vessels built for the Maritime Commission to Bureau Class, these including tugboats, barges, concrete cargo ships and wooden craft.

Early in the war time shipbuilding effort, the Bureau was forced to find larger Headquarters space in New York. Its old building at 24 Old Slip, occupied since 1927, was found to be inadequate and was sold. Another larger building nearby, at 47 Beaver Street, was accquired and utilized in its entirety. After alterations to this modern steel and concrete fireproof building were completed, the staff moved on April 7, 1941.

The advantage of these larger quarters was shortlived. Before the end of the war in 1945, the Bureau, again cramped for space, had to rent extra offices in another adjoining building. By then it became apparent that still larger permanent quarters was a necessity. Again, under the guidance of President Luckenbach, another site was sought. As a result, the eight story concrete and steel structure at 45 Broad Street was acquired. Renovations and modernization were completed, and the staff moved late in July, 1946. Here the entire sixth floor is devoted to executive offices, including a board room, meeting rooms, and a large library. The Hull Technical Staff occupies the entire fifth floor, while the Machinery Technical Staff has the entire fourth floor. The third floor is devoted entirely to the Report Section and the New York Surveying Staff. On the second floor is found the Main Files of the Bureau. On the first floor is the Accounting Department and the staff preparing the Bureau's annual ship register, *The Record*. In the basement a well equipped material testing laboratory is maintained.

Part of the entrance lobby
in the Bureau's
Headquarter's building

A committee
meeting room

The Board Room

The Library

*A part of
the testing laboratory*

Action in the testing laboratory

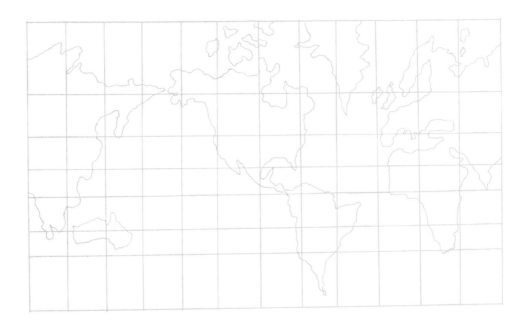

Expansion

Until shortly after World War II, the operations of the Bureau had been confined almost exclusively to the United States, with only a few of its own exclusive surveyors stationed in ports outside of the United States. Prior to the war, the arrangements with the British Corporation Register, the Registro Italiano Navale, and the Teikoku Kaiji Kyokai, coupled with the use of non-exclusive surveyors, had enabled adequate services to be provided to clients. Shortly after the war ended, developments in the United Kingdom

20

made it necessary to terminate the arrangement with the British Corporation Register, an arrangement which had proven mutually beneficial to both organizations for more than thirty years. The agreements had lapsed during the war and with the signing of the peace and the restoration of the activities of these two organizations, they were not renewed except on a very limited basis. They were confined to only those vessels having dual Classification, and then only in those cases where either one or the other society found it advantageous to avail itself of the services of the other.

The sale in large numbers of the surplus ships constructed in the United States under the war time building program had a very significant effect on the Bureau. All of these ships had been built, and were being maintained in Classification. It was very gratifying to note the success of our efforts to have Bureau Classification retained on a very large number of those sold for registry outside of the United States. The volume of work resulting enabled the Bureau to commence immediately the establishment of exclusive surveyors in many foreign ports. These developments were accompanied by a world-wide demand for new ships, many of which were contracted to be built outside of the United States by organizations which for years had their fleets Classed with the Bureau, and who specified Bureau Classification. The expansion of the offices already opened, and the establishment of new offices as a result of this work enabled the technical standards and the methods of operation of the Bureau to receive world-wide recognition to the end that there are now numbered among the clients many national shipping companies.

The Bureau now maintains exclusive surveyors at nearly all of the major seaports and shipbuilding centers, as well as in the steel producing and manufacturing areas. In addition, in order to provide prompt and efficient services for new construction or major repairs, technical offices are established in Genoa, London and Tokyo.

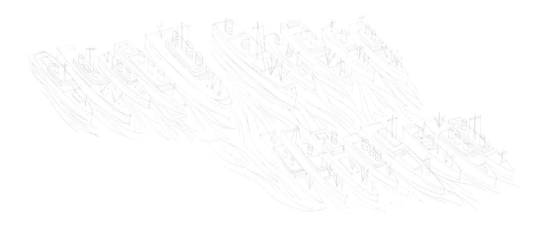

Vessels Existing in Class

During the postwar years the number and tonnage of vessels existing in Class with the Bureau reached an all-time high. A total of 8,221 vessels of 46,533,852 gross tons now exists in Class with the Bureau. These figures include both self-propelled and non-propelled vessels, and vessels registered in almost every maritime nation of the world. The great majority of these vessels are less than 20 years of age, and includes a large number constructed in the postwar years.

In most of the postwar years more tonnage has been completed to Bureau Class in shipyards abroad than in shipyards in the United States. The extent of this postwar trend is readily apparent from the figures in the following table. In some of these years as much as three to four times more gross tonnage was completed to Bureau Class in overseas shipyards than in United States shipyards. Part of this development, which did not exist before the war, is due to the fact that American shipping interests have been ordering tonnage built abroad for use in international and transoceanic

22

trade. However, a large portion of this tonnage has been for local national interests. For instance, a very large percentage of the vessels constructed in Italian shipyards for Italian shipowners, during the postwar years, has been to Bureau Class in addition to Class with the Registro Italiano. Similarly, in the early postwar years, much of the new merchant fleet constructed in Japan for Japanese shipowners was Classed by the Bureau. Many vessels built to Bureau requirements in France, Holland, Belgium, and West Germany have been for national interests in these countries. Other vessels have been constructed to Bureau Class for national interests in Turkey, the United Arab Republic, Argentina, Brasil, Spain, Taiwan, Israel, Canada, Kuwait, Surinam, Philippines, Pakistan, Denmark, Greece, Portugal, and England.

NUMBER, GROSS TONNAGE, AND HORSEPOWER OF MERCHANT VESSELS, INCLUDING BARGES, COMPLETED EACH YEAR TO AMERICAN BUREAU CLASS IN THE POST-WORLD WAR TWO PERIOD

Year	In United States Shipyards		In Overseas Shipyards		Total Each Year		
	No.	Gross Tons	No.	Gross Tons	No.	Gross Tons	Horsepower
1946	462	744,985	—	—	462	744,985	757,245
1947	304	338,733	3	16,173	307	354,906	356,502
1948	239	275,330	3	16,173	244	291,503	222,915
1949	226	644,417	10	46,280	236	690,697	511,733
1950	244	513,054	33	159,037	277	672,091	452,950
1951	260	285,708	55	359,328	315	645,036	492,982
1952	270	514,568	53	435,696	323	950,264	781,670
1953	424	712,070	74	713,637	498	1,425,707	1,312,047
1954	403	736,955	99	951,911	502	1,688,866	1,441,583
1955	384	335,798	81	746,588	465	1,082,386	715,190
1956	323	321,738	144	1,493,787	467	1,815,525	1,269,252
1957	399	541,062	133	1,761,866	532	2,302,928	1,566,345
1958	352	777,848	132	1,637,038	484	2,414,886	1,696,987
1959	432	748,719	124	1,793,240	556	2,541,959	1,665,311
1960	289	554,720	127	1,735,690	416	2,290,410	1,639,752
1961	262	554,824	98	1,554,512	360	2,109,336	1,606,585

Administrative Organization

Since its origin and throughout its growth, there have been many changes in the administrative organization of the American Bureau of Shipping. Since the time of reorganization in 1916, there have been only minor changes and, in this part, there is described the present organization as it is now operated under the provisions of the By-Laws, with some mention made of a few of the many distinguished persons who have held prominent positions in the administrative organization.

24

Organization

Under the original charter granted in 1862, the Corporation was granted the power to make and adopt a Constitution and By-Laws with authority to alter, modify, or repeal these from time to time. It was further stipulated that the business, property, and affairs of the Corporation shall be under the general control of a Board of Managers.

Under these broad provisions of the charter, numerous changes in the organization have taken place since it was granted. Upon the recommendation of the special committee appointed in 1916 to consider the question of the re-organization, a complete revision of the Constitution and By-Laws was made. Since then only minor changes have been made from time to time, these resulting in the presently established organization.

The Membership of the Bureau now numbers more than two hundred persons prominently identified with the shipping industry, these being ship owners, marine underwriters, shipbuilders, and the manufacturers of major propulsion components.

Elected from the Membership for terms of not less than one year nor more than three years is a Board of Managers now numbering thirty-nine, one third of whom are subject to re-election or replacement each year.

Elected annually by the Board of Managers from among its members is a committee of five designated as the Standing and Finance Committee. This committee has the power to regulate the loaning, investment, and other disposition of money, funds, stocks, and assets of the Bureau in any way it may deem conducive to the interests of the Bureau in accordance with the Charter and By-Laws. It is also encumbent on the executive officers of the Bureau to call upon this Committee from time to time for advice on all matters of importance relating to the Bureau's business.

In the By-Laws, provision is made for the following officers: a Chairman of the Board, a President, a Senior Vice-President, not more than five Vice-Presidents, not more than two Honorary Vice-Presidents, a Secretary, and a Treasurer. It is further provided that, at the discretion of the Board of Managers, the office of Chairman of the Board may be allowed to remain vacant. The officers are elected annually by the Board of Managers and, with the exception of Honorary Vice-Presidents, all are full-time salaried officers.

A Pension Committee composed of five members, of which the top ranking executive officer is one, is appointed annually subject to confirmation by the Board of Managers. This Committee has supervision of all matters relating to pensions and determines all questions relating thereto.

Subject to approval of the Board of Managers, Regional Committees may be appointed to review the operations of the Bureau in any specialized area. At the present time such Committees are established on the Pacific Coast, on the Great Lakes, and on the Western Rivers in the United States.

The Classification Committee is composed of at least thirteen members, nine of whom are appointed annually subject to confirmation by the Board of Managers. Four additional members are appointed monthly by the top ranking executive officer to serve in rotation for the period of two successive meetings. At present, this Committee meets twice each month. It has supervision of the reports of all surveyors, and it determines the class of rating of all vessels after due consideration of the recommendations of the surveyors.

The Bureau has numbered among its officers many persons outstanding in the shipping industry. In the early days the officers were for the most part recruited from the insurance interests, but since the reorganization in 1916, those honored by election to high offices in the organization have been recruited from other segments of the industry or, in the more recent years, from among the many who have made service with the Bureau almost their full working career.

From the inception of the American Shipmasters' Association in 1860, Mr. John D. Jones acted as Chairman until July 23, 1862, the date of the or-

26

ganization under the terms of the Charter, at which time he was elected President.

Following is a list of Presidents of the American Shipmasters' Association and the American Bureau of Shipping in chronological order:

AMERICAN SHIPMASTERS' ASSOCIATION

JOHN D. JONES	1862–1871
THEO. B. BLEECKER, JR.	1871–1879
HORACE J. MOODY	1879–1881
JOHN D. JONES	1881–1886
THEO. B. BLEECKER, JR.	1886–1898

AMERICAN BUREAU OF SHIPPING

Anton A. Raven	1899–1916
Stevenson Taylor	1916–1926
Charles A. McAllister	1926–1932
Executive V. P., J. Lewis Luckenbach	Acting during –1932
J. Lewis Luckenbach	1933–1950
Walter L. Green	1950–1957
David P. Brown	1957

Mr. Stevenson Taylor, who was elected President in 1916 as a result of the recommendation of the special committee established to consider the reorganization of the Bureau, had been a prominent shipbuilder and was well known in the industry for his valuable contributions towards the development of steam machinery for ship propulsion. Having completed ten years of service on March 1, 1926, he retired as President of the Bureau and was elected Chairman of the Board, a new office created as a mark of distinction for Mr. Taylor. He held this position until he passed away on May 19, 1926.

Captain Charles A. McAllister, who had retired as Engineer-in-Chief of the United States Coast Guard, and who had been responsible for many progressive developments in the design and construction of vessels for the Coast Guard fleet, was elevated from his position as Vice President of the Bureau, which position he had held following his retirement from government service, to succeed Mr. Taylor as President. Captain McAllister held this position until his death on January 6, 1932.

Mr. J. Lewis Luckenbach, a well known figure among the leading shipowners of the world, who had five years previously severed his connections with the shipowners segment of the industry to accept the position of Vice President of the Bureau, assumed the duties of President for the balance of the year 1932, and he was elected President in 1933. Mr. Luckenbach continued as President until 1950 when he was elected Chairman of the Board at which time he relinquished the office of President. He remained as Chairman of the Board until his death on July 4, 1951.

Mr. Walter L. Green, who a few years previously had been elected a Vice President of the Bureau, following a distinguished career first in the ship operation business, and during and for a short time after World War II, in the shipbuilding business, was elected President of the Bureau to succeed Mr. Luckenbach. In 1952, he was also named Chairman of the Board. In 1957, he relinquished the position of President, remaining as Chairman until his retirement on July 31, 1959. In appreciation of his very valuable services to the Bureau, Mr. Green was elected an Honorary Vice President upon his retirement.

Mr. David P. Brown, who, after having served almost his entire business career with the Bureau, had been successively elevated to the position of Senior Vice President and Technical Manager, was elected President to succeed Mr. Green on January 29, 1957.

JOHN D. JONES
A Founder, 1862
President: 1862–1871; 1881–1886

THEO. B. BLEECKER, JR.
President: 1871–1879; 1886–1898

ANTON A. RAVEN
President: 1898–1916

STEVENSON TAYLOR
President: 1916–1926
Chairman of the Board
March 1, 1926 to May 19, 1926

Captain CHARLES A. MCALLISTER
President: 1926–1932

J. LEWIS LUCKENBACH
President: 1933–1950
Chairman of the Board of Managers 1950–1951

WALTER L. GREEN
President: 1950–1957
Chairman of the Board of Managers 1952–1959

DAVID P. BROWN
President: 1957–

3

Administrative Activities

The American Bureau of Shipping endeavors to aid in the development of waterborne commerce, both domestic and international.

In this connection there are provided certain services, along with incentive or recognition awards, to those engaged in these activities, or to those planning to enter the marine field. These services and awards are described in the following pages.

33

Educational Prizes

On January 29, 1924, the American Bureau of Shipping established an Annual Educational Prize. A system of cash prize awards was devised at various American institutes where the subjects of naval architecture and marine engineering are taught. The faculty of the institution, or a committee of the main faculty, was established as the determining group in selecting the student to whom the award is made.

At the Massachusetts Institute of Technology and the University of Michigan College of Engineering, the American Bureau of Shipping prize is awarded for general excellence in the last two years of study in the course in naval architecture and marine engineering.

A similar prize is given the graduating midshipman who stands highest in the mechanical drafting and descriptive geometry course in the Department of Marine Engineering at the United States Naval Academy.

34

Similarly, the prize is awarded to the graduating student at the United States Merchant Marine Academy, Kings Point, New York, who stands highest in scholastic work, character, leadership and participation in extra-curricular activities.

At the New York State Maritime College, Fort Schuyler, New York, the prize is given for proficiency in engineering to a graduating student.

For the highest combined average in naval architecture, mathematics and physics at the Maine Maritime Academy, Castine, Maine, the prize is given to a member of the graduating class each year.

At the Webb Institute of Naval Architecture, Glen Cove, Long Island, New York, the Bureau's prize is awarded for the highest average scholarship achieved during the junior and senior years.

This American Bureau of Shipping Scholarship prize has been awarded also, in the past, to students at other universities, including the University of California, Cornell University, and Lehigh University.

The Board of Managers of the American Bureau of Shipping in October, 1927, founded the "Stevenson Taylor Memorial Scholarship" at the Massachusetts Institute of Technology. This was established as a memorial to the late Stevenson Taylor, President of the Bureau from 1916 to 1926. In more recent years, this has been transformed into the "Stevenson Taylor Memorial Prize" and is given for the best thesis on marine engineering. It is awarded each year to a member of the graduating class of Webb Institute of Naval Architecture.

Also established as a memorial, "The Captain Charles A. McAllister Prize" for proficiency in engineering is awarded yearly to a graduating student at the United States Coast Guard Academy, New London, Connecticut. This prize honors the late Captain Charles A. McAllister, a graduate of the Coast Guard Academy, and President of the American Bureau of Shipping from 1926 until 1932.

35

Captain GEORGE FRIED
First Recipient of the
Bureau Medal of Valor 1929

Captain GILES C. STEDMAN
Second Recipient of the
Bureau Medal of Valor 1933

Captain HENRIK KURT CARLSEN
Third Recipient of the
Bureau Medal of Valor 1952

Valor Medal
American Bureau of Shipping
for
"Acts or Deeds of Valor
Beyond the Call of Duty"

Valor Medal

In 1928, the American Bureau of Shipping, believing that some recognition for acts or deeds of valor should be given to seagoing personnel, instituted a policy of awarding a Valor Medal. This distinctive medal is now awarded by the Bureau on rare occasions, and only in laudable cases for deeds of exceptional valor beyond the call of duty when an American vessel renders service to another vessel in distress, or is rendered such service by a vessel of any other nationality. Due to the small number of these gold

Valor Medals in existence, and to the high qualifications necessary to merit the decoration, it is a highly prized and extremely valued honor.

The Valor Medal was presented on March 17, 1952, to Captain Henrik Kurt Carlsen, heroic skipper of the Isbrandtsen Company C-1 type cargo ship *Flying Enterprise,* which was lost in the North Atlantic during January of that year.

Presentation ceremonies were held in the Board Room of the Bureau's main office in New York, with Mr. Walter L. Green, then Chairman of the Board and President, officiating.

Captain Carlsen was highly praised for his gallant and lone effort to save his ship, in a presentation speech made by Mr. Green. The late Captain Roger Williams of the Newport News Shipbuilding and Dry Dock Company was Chairman of the Committee of Award appointed by the Board of Managers of the American Bureau. Also on this Committee was Vice Admiral Merlin O'Neill, Commandant, United States Coast Guard, and Mr. Owen C. Torrey of the Marine Office of America.

A gathering of one hundred Members of the American Bureau of Shipping and Isbrandtsen Company officials witnessed the award ceremonies, and participated in a buffet luncheon which followed.

On only two previous occasions has this highly valued decoration been awarded. The previous award was made in 1933, when it was given to the late Rear Admiral, then Captain, Giles C. Stedman, Master of the S. S. *American Merchant* of the United States Lines, for his heroic act in the rescue of the crew of the British ship *Exeter City* on January 20, 1933. The first Valor Medal was awarded on January 29, 1929, to the late Captain George Fried, then Master of the United States Lines operated S. S. *America*, predecessor of the current S. S. *America*, for his outstanding actions in connection with the rescue of the crews of the *Florida*, owned by A. T. Rosasco, Genoa, Italy, and the British vessel *Antinoe*, of New Egypt and Levant Shipping Company.

38

Ship Register

As stated in the Constitution and By-laws, one of the objectives of the American Bureau of Shipping is to provide for shipowners, shipbuilders, underwriters, shippers, and all interested in maritime commerce, a faithful and accurate

Classification and Registry of Mercantile Shipping, and the "dissemination of information upon subjects of marine and commercial interest." To this end there is published annually the *Record of the American Bureau of Shipping*.

The preparation of the "Record" constitutes an important part of the work of the Bureau. This "Record" is widely purchased by shipowners, shipbuilders, shippers, and underwriters and, with its semi-monthly supplements, forms a reference work through which the interested parties can determine the character and seaworthiness of any Classed vessel which they propose to purchase, charter, or insure, or in which they propose to transport cargo.

The 1962 issue, the 94th annual volume of the *Record of the American Bureau of Shipping*, is now being distributed to subscribers in practically every maritime nation of the world. This edition of the Bureau's Ship Register contains over 1,800 pages, and lists more than 20,500 vessels, including all American Bureau Classed vessels. Illustrations are included of typical inboard profiles of certain types of vessels listed in the "Record," including the principal war built vessels constructed for the United States Government.

The "Record" is kept up-to-date by supplements. All additions and known changes that have occurred since the publication of the "Record" appear in the supplements that are issued to subscribers twice a month. These changes and additions are covered by a complete index that is revised with each issue of the supplement. The index not only covers vessels that have been added since the publication of the "Record," but also includes any known change that might affect the status of a vessel that has already appeared in the "Record" or supplements. A separate index covering additional owners is also included.

Special reports giving the latest survey data on Classed vessels together with reports of change of name, flag, tonnage and ownership of all vessels that appear in the front section of the "Record," are sent daily to customers who subscribe for that service.

40

Classification, date of latest surveys of hull, machinery and boilers, date of last tailshaft drawing and last drydocking are shown in the "Record" on Classed vessels. Latest information is supplied by the supplements.

The principal characteristics of each vessel are shown. Included is such information relative to the ship, as official number and signal letters; name of vessel and all former names; name of owner and address; flag and port of registry; type of vessel (Tw.Sc.Pass., etc.); location of machinery (aft, etc.); material (steel, wood, etc.); system of framing; number of decks; number of bulkheads, type, and deck to which they extend; tanks available for water ballast; number of hatches and size of largest hatch; number of holds and length of longest hold; number and length of cargo tanks on tankers; fuel and capacity; navigational aids; equipment numeral; molded and registered dimensions; draft and freeboard; deck erections; bale cubic of refrigerated spaces and system of refrigeration; bale cubic capacity of cargo spaces; deadrise of bottom and depth of rubbing keel; gross, net and deadweight tonnage (when available); builder's hull number; builder's name, where built, and year of build; engine builder and date of build; boiler builder and date of build; type of engines and boilers; horsepower of main propulsion machinery; heating surface and working pressure; draft (forced or induced); reduction gears; system of injection (internal combustion engines).

In the back of the "Record" considerable additional information is to be found. Included is an index to compound names of vessels, alphabetical by last name; changed names, alphabetically indexed by all former names; list of owners and their addresses, showing name of vessels under their ownership; name, cable address and location of shipyards and ship repair plants, giving the sizes and capacities of drydocks and marine railways; builders of machinery and boilers.

Included in a special section is a complete list of all self-propelled steel merchant vessels of 2,000 gross tons and over, constructed by each shipbuilder in the United States, beginning in 1914 and extending through 1961.

41

The Bulletin

The Bureau has for many years distributed a monthly publication entitled *The Bulletin* to the shipping and shipbuilding industries, and allied trades, in the United States and abroad. Over 2,600 copies are mailed each month, of which 1,000 go to interests abroad. A record of the vessels on order, building, launched and completed to Bureau Class requirements in the United States and abroad is shown each month. Statistical data on shipping and shipbuilding throughout the world is published each month, including data on the various national fleets.

An up-to-date list of the offices maintained by the Bureau in all nations is printed each month, together with names of the surveyors stationed at each of these ports. Additional information, such as the many technical committees established by the Bureau abroad and in the United States, is published on occasion, together with a complete report on the Annual Meeting of the Members and of the Board of Managers, and the Semi-Annual Meeting of the Board of Managers.

42

Reference Library

Maintained at the Headquarters building of the Bureau in New York is a technical reference library of more than 3,000 volumes for the use of the Technical Staff, but available generally to the maritime industry. Here are to be found a great many engineering text books bearing on machinery, steel, welding, naval architecture, and marine engineering.

The yearly published technical transactions of the great engineering societies of the world, which fill a large number of shelves, are carefully preserved and cataloged.

Monthly shipbuilding and marine engineering magazines are bound in volumes at the end of each year and preserved.

The various yearly ship registers of the world, as published by national classification societies, are to be found here in a large collection dating well back into the nineteenth century. Also available are the *Rules for the Building and Classing of Steel Vessels* as issued from time to time by these societies.

There is a large collection of maritime historical books. These cover the sailing ship era, the introduction of steam propulsion, the luxury transatlantic passenger liners, and the super size oil tankers and ore carriers of the present time.

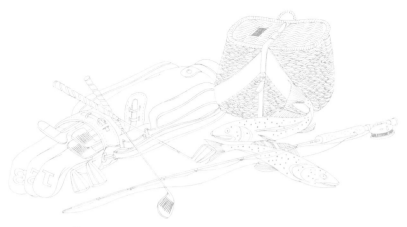

Social Benefits

Years ago management recognized the value of social benefits which provide protection to the Bureau's employees and their families. In 1919, long before the Federal Social Security program was formulated, a Bureau pension fund was inaugurated, and, in subsequent years, the original modest sum provided was augmented from time to time. At the Annual Meeting of the Board of Managers on January 27, 1925, an informal pension plan was adopted to take effect on February 1, 1925, and a Pension Committee was formed to administer it. At that time, the plan was non-contributory, and management was foresighted enough to provide for the computation of pensions on the average salary for the five years preceding retirement, which today is a fairly universal procedure, since it protects the employees to the extent that retirement income is based on current salary standards rather than on life-time average, thus acting as a hedge against inflationary periods, rising standards, promotions, etc.

It was felt, in 1938, that the informal self-administered plan should be replaced with a formal plan administered by an insurance company. Accordingly, in May, 1938, the Standing and Finance Committee, through the Pension Committee, authorized the adoption of such a plan, which was partially on a contributory basis. Basically, the plan provided for the purchase of an annuity related to the employee's salary.

44

Recognizing that some employees who were on the staff as of July 1, 1938, would not obtain the desired benefits, the management authorized the purchase of past service annuities. These purchases were consummated during the period 1938 through 1943.

It became apparent, by 1948, that rising standards of living, inflation and staff promotions tended to lessen the value of an annuity under the regular pension plan. Consequently, a supplemental retirement plan was established to augment the benefits received under the regular plan. The supplemental retirement plan is funded under a bank trusteeship and provides for the payment of a differential necessary to bring the total pension payments to an established minimum. The supplemental plan has required the transfer to the trustees of substantial sums to provide sufficient reserves to assure the payment of present and future pensions.

Group insurance, both life, hospital and surgical, has also received the attention of management. In October, 1924, this phase of fringe benefits was inaugurated when employees were covered by group life insurance. A unique feature of the group life insurance policy is the total or permanent disability clause which is not normally written into new group policies. Since it was made part of the original policy coverage, it has been continued. It is also interesting to point out that retirement does not lapse coverage, although the amount of insurance is gradually reduced.

The group insurance plan was expanded in 1942 to take into account coverage for hospitalization and surgery, including coverage for employees' dependents.

The foregoing plans apply only to American and Canadian employees. However, as a result of the Bureau's world wide expansion during the postwar period, many foreign nationals have been employed in our overseas offices, and, in 1953, a foreign national employees' benefit plan was put into effect patterned after the domestic plan.

Technical Organization

The primary duties of a ship classification society can be performed only through the efficient operation of its technical staff, and the soundness of the technical requirements established and administered by that staff. In this part there is contained a description of the technical organization of the Bureau as it exists today, following the many changes and developments which have taken place through the one hundred years of the Bureau's existence.

While for the purposes of this presentation, it might appear that there is a sharp distinction between the technical and administrative organizations, nevertheless it should be noted that this is not true. Reference to Part 2 will show that in more recent times, including the present, many of the administrative officers have either brought to the Bureau sound technical abilities, or have spent a considerable portion of their business career in the technical organization of the Bureau.

46

Surveying Staff

The operations of the American Bureau of Shipping in providing the services required in its functions as a ship Classification society, such as the carrying out of surveys on the hulls and machinery of ships under construction or already in service, the testing of materials, the analysis and recording of reports, approval of plans for hulls and machinery, the formation of the "Rules", and the conduct of research, etc., come under the direct control of the Chief Surveyor's establishment. This establishment consists of the offices of the Chief Surveyor, Chief Surveyor-Hull, Chief Surveyor-Machinery, and Chief Surveyor-Operations. Each of the last mentioned have specialized areas of control, but all dovetail together. All operations performed by the large staff of surveyors maintained in nearly all of the principal seaports and in the shipbuilding and manufacturing areas of the world, as well as services provided by the Hull and Machinery Technical Departments, come under the direction of this establishment.

The Bureau is proud that the office of Chief Surveyor has been held by so many persons outstanding in their profession, both nationally and internationally, and who have contributed so much to the shipping industry.

Shortly after the reorganization in 1916, Mr. George G. Sharp was appointed Chief Surveyor. He held this position until 1919 when he resigned to establish his own business as a private naval architect. Since that time, his name has been associated with the design of many outstanding ships, and the concern bearing his name is well known throughout marine circles.

Mr. Edward G. Tuck succeeded Mr. Sharp. He held the position until 1924 when he resigned to take up private surveying activities.

Mr. David Arnott, who had served as Deputy Chief Surveyor under both Mr. Sharp and Mr. Tuck, and who had brought to the Bureau much valuable experience in both field and technical operations by virtue of previous service with the British Corporation Register of Shipping, was appointed Chief Surveyor to succeed Mr. Tuck. In 1938, Mr. Arnott was honored by being elected a Vice President with the titles of Vice President and Chief Surveyor, which positions he held until his retirement in 1947.

He was succeeded as Chief Surveyor by Mr. David P. Brown, our current President, who was also elected a Vice President in 1950. Mr. Lewis C. Host was appointed to the position of Chief Surveyor in 1952. Mr. Host held the position until 1957, when he was elected a Vice President, and subsequently Senior Vice President, the position he now holds.

There have been numerous changes in the organization of the Chief Surveyor's control establishment as the Bureau's business has expanded both in volume and in complexity. A few years back it consisted of only the Chief Surveyor and a Chief Engineer Surveyor. This latter position was held by Mr. Arthur R. Gatewood until 1957 when he was elected a Vice President, the position he now holds.

Technical Committees

The Bureau maintains an organization of technical committees headed by a committee prescribed in the By-Laws and known as The Technical Committee. This committee is composed of persons conversant with maritime affairs, eminent in the science of naval architecture and marine engineering. Members are appointed subject to confirmation by the Board of Man-

48

agers. This committee has supervision of the "Rules" and all details relative to the building, surveying, and classification of vessels, the rules for issuing certificates of vessels and all appurtenances, and the form of such certificates.

Operating under this committee are the Committee on Naval Architecture and the Committee on Engineering. In turn there are maintained subcommittees to deal with such specialized subjects as welding, materials, electrical installations, etc.

In recognition of the fact that there are many technical problems peculiar to vessels operating on the Great Lakes and on the Western Rivers of the United States, special technical committees are maintained for those areas.

Likewise, when the Bureau was faced with the rapid expansion of its activities to areas outside of the United States, it was appreciated that the "Rules" might reflect too strongly, and in some cases unnecessarily, procedures and practices in the United States. As a result, technical committees were established in Italy, France, Belgium, the Netherlands, and the United Kingdom.

Of late years, there has been evinced considerable interest in the use of nuclear power for ships, and, in recognition of the complexities of the problems which might be encountered, a Committee on Nuclear Applications has been established. This committee is composed of leading experts in the fields of nuclear science and engineering, and it will be able to analyze and appraise any proposals submitted to the Bureau.

In addition to ordinary technical problems which can be processed through this organization of standing committees, whether these problems are real or general in nature, there sometimes arise very specialized problems, such as those relating to reduction gears, propeller design, refrigeration, etc. In such cases, it is the practice to convene special panels of experts in the particular field affected, and thus extend the scope of the work of the various committees.

Technical Activities

Since the inception of the American Bureau of Shipping one hundred years ago, vast studies have been made in waterborne transport. In the early days of the Bureau's lifetime, merchant ships were all of moderate size, built of wood, and conformed to more or less standardized types. Mechanical propulsion was as yet unknown, and when rules were first published establishing the requirements for Classification, these were quite properly very general and broadly empirical in nature. With the advent of the use of iron, and shortly thereafter the use of steel, as the more popular materials for hull construction, and with the attendant increase in size and variations in types of ships, the "Rules" of the Bureau were continually revised. Also, with the increasing dependence upon mechanical propulsion, the "Rules" were expanded to include requirements for those mechanical items upon which depended the safety, and the ability to perform reliably the services for which the ships were intended.

Many items which today are considered commonplace have had their birth within the lifetime of the Bureau, and there are some, still in their infancy, in which the Bureau has had, or will continue to have active participation, in order that its services as a Classification Society may not be second to any other society.

In this part there is presented a very brief review of only some of these many and varied activities.

50

The Metallurgical Laboratory

Before the advent of welding in ship construction there was no great necessity for the Bureau to maintain a metallurgical laboratory. Any investigations required of the failure of shipbuilding materials were normally carried out for the Bureau by independent laboratories. However, with the increased use of welded construction in the late 1930's, a Bureau laboratory, on a very modest scale, was initiated to investigate weld samples submitted by the various shipyards in connection with obtaining approval of welding processes, procedures and joint designs.

The requirement for a larger and completely equipped metallurgical laboratory was given great impetus as a result of the structural failures that occurred in some of the ships built during World War Two, and by the

Bureau's desire to carry out its own investigations on plating removed from these vessels. When the Bureau's headquarters were moved to 45 Broad Street in 1946, a large portion of the basement area was allotted for laboratory purposes. A complete machine shop for the preparation of tensile, bend, impact and fatigue specimens was installed, together with all essential laboratory equipment, such as tensile, impact and fatigue machines, various types of hardness testers, research model microscope, micro-projector, photographic equipment, heat treating furnaces, hot etching facilities, welding machine, and strain gauge equipment.

Investigations of fractured hull steel plating and of plate samples submitted by shipyards and steel producers have been major projects of the metallurgical laboratory. The results of the Bureau's own research, together with that carried out by various Government agencies and by private industry, were the basis on which the Bureau's Subcommittee on Materials formulated the 1947 specifications for hull structural steel, and their subsequent revisions, to obtain greater notch toughness in ship steel plating. Investigations of steel produced abroad to their own specifications have led to the approval of material manufactured to requirements differing from those prescribed in the "Rules." Investigations of steel produced by new steel making processes, the study of the effect of different compositions and heat treatments, and studies on various types of notch toughness tests are continuing projects of the metallurgical department.

In 1948 an investigation sponsored by the Welding Research Council was initiated in the Bureau's laboratory to evaluate the effects of some of the many variables involved in peening welds. The results of this research were published in the August, 1953, *Welding Journal Research Supplement* in an article entitled "An Investigation on Peening" which has been helpful in supplementing code requirements dealing with peening variables.

In the field of machinery materials, metallurgical investigations have been made of failures of gears, shafts, boiler plating, propellers, etc. The results

52

of Bureau research on welding procedures and stress corrosion cracking were of considerable help to the American Bureau of Shipping Propeller Panel in drafting the *Guidance Manual for Making Manganese Bronze Propeller Repairs,* issued in 1954. A current investigation of various propeller materials is concerned with determining some of their mechanical properties not covered by present specifications. It is expected that this information will be of considerable interest to those concerned with the design and use of marine propellers.

Tailshaft failures have long been a source of serious concern to the Bureau, and numerous investigations have been carried out to determine the cause of these failures and the properties of the material involved. A research program, initiated several years ago, is being carried out in the Bureau's laboratory on miniature tailshaft assemblies having one inch diameter shafts, to study the major variables involved in service tailshaft failures. Specially designed fatigue machines are being used to determine the rotary bending endurance limit of these assemblies under different test conditions. The effects of force fit and shrink fit allowances, liner thickness, liner to hub spacing, relief grooves, etc., are being investigated. It is expected that the results obtained can be used to advantage in planning large scale tests, or even in present production designs.

The Bureau's metallurgical laboratory is not intended, nor has it been used in any way, to compete with the business of private commercial laboratories. It is maintained for the Bureau's own benefit, and represents part of the Classification service to owners and builders of merchant vessels. With the probable future use of new hull and machinery materials, the value of maintaining a metallurgical laboratory should become of increasing importance.

Hull Structural Steel

Hull structural steel specified by classification society "Rules" for many years had proven adequate for ships of riveted construction. The only criteria for acceptance were the tensile strength and ductility as measured by simple tensile and bend tests, no reference being made to composition, deoxidation practice, or notch toughness properties. It was only after the almost complete structural failure of a new T2 tanker at the builder's pier in January, 1943, that investigation of the hull steel focused attention on another property of steel not heretofore determined by routine tests, namely notch toughness.

Reports of the service experience of many of the all-welded ships built during World War Two and since showed clearly that they were much more sensitive to notches than were riveted ships. There were several, although not proven explanations given for this behavior, such as the monolithic nature of the welded hull, triaxial stresses, low temperatures, geometry of certain details, or stresses resulting from erection or welding sequences. Considerable attention was given to details, and a minimum number of riveted connections were introduced in later ships, resulting in greatly improved performance, but brittle fractures continued to occur in the older all-welded

54

ships. Studies of these reports showed that thicker plates were more prone to brittle fracture than were thin plates. This tendency has been ascribed to the ability of thinner plates to buckle more easily, the greater triaxiality of stress in the thick plate, and the metallurgical benefit to the steel by rolling to lesser thicknesses. The range of thicknesses with which this experience had been gained was almost all below ⅞ inch.

During the war emergency it was not possible to make changes in steel specifications, but after hostilities ceased the Bureau established its Special Subcommittee-Materials to consider the problem of hull structural steel. This committee proposed in 1947 that three classes of hull plates be adopted with a view to obtaining approximately uniform toughness in all thicknesses, that is, to provide one quality. These classes were based upon thickness: Class A being for shapes and for plates up to and including ½ inch and involving no change from former rules, except that limits were placed on impurities; Class B covered plates in the range over ½ inch to 1 inch inclusive, and specified, in addition, composition, particularly as to maximum carbon and a range of manganese; Class C, for plates above 1 inch thick, specified the deoxidation practice as well as composition. These classes first appeared in the 1948 "Rules." The rather restrictive requirements for Class C had the purpose of maintaining an acceptable notch toughness in plates of thicknesses beyond the range of most of the service experience. As the size of vessels increased rapidly, it was decided in 1953 to limit Class C to 1⅜ inches maximum thickness, and to require special specifications above that figure. Plates made to Class C specifications, and normalized after rolling, are now accepted for thicknesses over 1⅜ inches to 2 inches inclusive.

By specifying plates by thickness only, without reference to application, special marking and segregating of plates in the shipyards was minimized. Time was allowed for the gradual adoption of the new "Rules" for steel, and vessels building, or for which steel had already been ordered, were Classed on the basis of "Rules" in effect at the time of contracting.

Failure of two foreign built vessels having steel almost complying with the Class B specifications, and in thicknesses within or just over the ½ inch to 1 inch range, led to the adoption of an increase in manganese requirement for this class in the 1956 "Rules."

Since the adoption of these steel specifications, there have been no brittle failures of any kind where the material has conformed to the specifications, and it has been possible to permit some relaxation in their application in areas where quality of material is less critical. Alternate specifications now permit steel having a manganese-carbon ratio of 2.5 or more to be used in certain non-critical areas with the owner's approval; and where the steel maker offers an acceptable program of notch toughness testing, the composition and deoxidation requirements of material up to $1\frac{3}{8}$ inches inclusive may be modified.

Other classification societies followed the Bureau's lead in subsequent years, some at first by merely requiring hull steel to be "specially approved" without a specification, but with control on application. There was some resistance to the adoption of the new Bureau "Rules," especially in areas where production cost was high and capacity limited for making the fully-killed steel called for by Class C. The other classification societies followed somewhat the same pattern as the Bureau, having variations in the severity of the specifications with thickness, but with the important difference that, whereas the Bureau's requirements were based on obtaining the desired notch toughness by controlling the chemical composition and deoxidation practice, several of the other societies' requirements were written around tests for notch toughness without regard to composition or deoxidation practice. In addition to the three classes adopted by the Bureau, some of the other societies provided for elimination of the riveted connections otherwise required by substitution of strakes of more notch-tough steel.

Altogether, there were among the societies some 22 different specifications for hull steel in effect, and it is not surprising that shipbuilders and repair yards, as well as steel makers and ship owners, began to urge the classification societies to adopt uniform requirements. It is a tribute to the effectiveness of the societies that the number of steel specifications has been reduced from 22 to 5 by their joint action.

That action was initiated in 1952 by Det Norske Veritas which suggested that the technical heads of several of the classification societies, who were then in Gothenburg for a meeting of the International Institute of Welding, might discuss the question informally. Following that meeting, a similar one was held in 1955 in Zurich, and another in London in 1957 at which it was agreed that a working party of representatives of each society would try to reach a definite agreement. After voluminous correspondence and two meetings in early 1958, this working party agreed upon a set of requirements which they could recommend to the committees of their respective societies. These requirements contained substantially all the specifications of the Bureau's three classes, but included a grade based on notch toughness testing rather than composition, acceptable to the Bureau up to 1⅜ inches inclusive, and a further grade of more notch-tough material to be used in the absence of riveted seams otherwise required. (This latter grade is not covered in the Bureau's "Rules" since some riveting is now required in all vessels above certain sizes.) In September 1958, a Special Panel of the Bureau's Subcommittee on Materials considered the draft agreement and, as a result, modifications were made to the Bureau's "Rules" in order to implement those parts acceptable to the Bureau.

At a meeting of the classification societies in London in 1959, the unified specifications were discussed and, with minor reservations as to details by several of the participants, were agreed upon as a basis for hull steel rules.

Application of the various grades within any particular ship was not considered, and there is presently some variation among the societies with respect to plate thickness, location and extent, as well as type of vessel to which each of the grades of the unified specifications are applied.

57

Welding in Shipbuilding

During World War One there were some far-sighted individuals in the United States who envisaged the possibilities of utilizing welding for connecting the components of a ship's structure, and a design for a moderate size cargo vessel was prepared. Work was actually commenced on one such vessel. However, following the early cessation of hostilities, this project was discontinued and this first ship was never completed.

58

The Bureau took an active part in this project, and in 1927 there first appeared in the *Rules for Building and Classing Steel Vessels* tentative rules for electric and gas welding in hull construction, but these confined the use of welding to parts of relatively minor structural importance. In the early 1930's, designers and builders were eager to make use of possible savings in cost and weight that might be obtained by the use of this method of fabricating hull structures. Numerous designs were developed, and experience was gained with the welding process. The Bureau actively encouraged these developments and Classed a number of craft, mostly barges, with the added note in the classification "Metal Arc Welded" or "Carbon Arc Welded." A paper read before The Society of Naval Architects and Marine Engineers in 1934 by the then Chief Surveyor, Mr. David Arnott, entitled "Some Examples of Welded Ship Construction", describes several of these vessels.

The 1936 "Rules" were the first to state that welding would be accepted for all parts of the hull. By that time the "Rules" contained detailed requirements for the approval of electrodes and the qualification of welding operators. The latter were adopted in recognition of the importance of workmanship to the quality of the finished weld, means of inspection then being limited. In 1936, the first automatic machine welding process was approved.

In large ocean going ships, welding was at first applied to the internal structure, with some riveting retained in the shell and sometimes in the deck. By 1937, the Bureau was surveying oil tankers of over 18,000 deadweight tons having their entire tank space of welded construction.

The first of the cargo vessels designed by the Maritime Commission in the late 1930's provided for either riveted or welded construction. While some of the builders employed riveting for certain connections which lent themselves to facilitating erection, or merely to utilize existing skills and manpower, other yards made use of welding exclusively. Thus, when the war emergency reached the United States, the Bureau was prepared to deal with

59

the greatly expanded program of shipbuilding carried out largely in new yards equipped only for welding.

When failures occurred in a few of the welded ships (notably a Great Lakes bulk freighter, a T2 tanker, and several Liberty type cargo ships), an intensive study was begun and continued throughout the building program. A Special Subcommittee-Welding, consisting of metallurgists and shipyard welding supervisory personnel, was formed by the Bureau in 1943. With the guidance of this committee, a booklet emphasizing the importance of design details and workmanship which had been shown by the studies to have contributed to the failures, was prepared, and widely distributed. Brittle fractures were drastically reduced, largely through control of details, and while there still were catastrophic failures, they were very few in number compared with the total number of ships in operation under adverse conditions. There is no question that the hitherto unheard-of mass production of ships by the United States throughout the war period was possible only through the adoption of welding on an unprecedented scale.

This program afforded a basis for statistical studies not likely to be repeated. Perhaps the most pronounced trend derived from these studies was the apparent effect of a minimum amount of riveting in inhibiting brittle fractures. The later designs of war-time cargo ships had only one riveted connection and careful treatment of design details. These ships continue to operate with almost complete freedom from structural failure. This and the other lessons learned from that invaluable opportunity have been embodied in the "Rules" and in the control of details obtained through plan approval.

Light Metals in Shipbuilding

The aluminum alloys, or the "light metals" as they are frequently referred to, have had a fantastic history. Pure aluminum is a rare sight owing to its great affinity for oxygen. However, only a century ago, aluminum, even when isolated in the oxidized form, was considered a novelty. Little was it realized that this elusive metal would, upon being alloyed with other metals, have properties considered necessary to meet the rugged requirements of a marine structural material. Nor was it realized that one day entire barges would be constructed of this material, or that the hull and superstructure of a special type of craft, destined to be the fastest vessel afloat, would be built of aluminum alloy material.

Aluminum found its way into literally hundreds of alloys, and it is not surprising, therefore, that some retardation resulted in their development owing

61

to the confusion in the selection of alloys best suited to marine application. Additional hindrance in development of the marine alloys was caused by World War Two which occurred just as considerable new alloy development was in progress. During the war, all available aluminum alloy material flowed into channels unrelated to the marine field. Still further hindrance can be attributed to the initial cost of these alloys which, when combined with additional fabrication costs, confined them to the experimental and luxury type of craft.

A brief review of the properties of these alloys, as we know them today, readily explains their attractiveness for marine purposes. Aluminum alloys weigh approximately one-third the weight of a similar volume of steel. They exhibit good strength, are easily worked and joined by all the usual methods, are non-magnetic and non-sparking, and are highly resistant to corrosion from sea water. Not all of these properties were appreciated during aluminum's early history. Nevertheless, even before the turn of the century, there was at least one major attempt to build a small seagoing vessel with this type of material.

Not a great deal of progress was made until the years immediately following World War Two, when it became apparent that there was available an alloy which had most of the desirable properties. At this time, a considerable effort was made toward the practical application of this alloy. The American Bureau's position in respect to this new development was always one of continued interest and complete cooperation in the proposals made by designers and builders. At that time two design offices submitted proposals for new ocean ore carriers in the 330 foot and 400 foot length range, both of which were to be of all-aluminum alloy construction. The American Bureau's Hull Technical Staff contributed to these efforts by offering extensive comments on both designs. About this same time the Bureau also cooperated in testing riveted aluminum alloy connections. A large all riveted aluminum box girder arrangement was subjected to hydrostatic test loading to simulate riveted deep

62

tank and shell connections under load. The results pointed emphatically to one major difficulty with riveted aluminum construction: namely, the inability to satisfactorily caulk this type of material.

Since the material in question was a heat-treatable alloy, it did not lend itself to welded connections where strength of the welded joint was a major factor. Consequently, it appeared that this alloy would be confined to above-water applications. Notwithstanding this apparent handicap, efforts continued to use this material in relatively small applications, and the American Bureau approved its use for a riveted upper house and stack installation on the Delta Line (Mississippi Shipping Company) vessels, *Del Sud* and *Del Mar*, built to Class by the Ingalls Shipbuilding Corporation in 1947.

These vessels were followed by a similar type but far more extensive installation aboard the American President Lines vessels *President Wilson* and *President Cleveland*, both of which were Classed American Bureau. The Bureau's Technical Staff devoted considerable time to the matter of scantlings for the long deck houses on these vessels, as well as to the method of joining and insulating between the steel and aluminum materials.

By this time the weight savings feature gave rise to a considerable interest in the use of light metals for topside structures on passenger vessels, where it could be used to great advantage with respect to stability characteristics. The S.S. *United States*, completed in 1952 by the Newport News Shipbuilding and Dry Dock Company, is an excellent example of a very extensive topside installation of aluminum alloy material. The Bureau cooperated to the utmost in helping to settle the problems arising in connection with suitable scantlings, and in such other problems as the handling of materials at the producers' mills, the special handling of aluminum rivets, the developing of details for insulating joints between dissimilar metals, and the making of numerous special connections. The success of the *United States* speaks well for the care which was exercised in her design and construction, and particularly the practicability of using aluminum alloy material on a large scale installation.

The aluminum producers in the United States and elsewhere were aware of the need for an alloy which had all the desirable properties and which, in addition, could be welded without appreciable loss of strength in the weld zone. They have succeeded in developing a series of alloys which satisfy these requirements. The development of this group of non-heat-treatable alloys represents a decided turning point in the growth of aluminum alloys as applied to marine usage. They made possible satisfactory welded connections, and thereby not only overcame the previous difficulty with caulking, but made possible the general application of welded construction which is more economical than riveted construction. These new alloys would appear to represent a major advance in the possible use of aluminum alloys for marine structures.

The American Bureau has always taken an active interest in new developments and in research work in general. Consequently, it was only natural that the Bureau be represented on the Society of Naval Architects and Marine Engineers' Panel S-11, "Aluminum for Ship Structures," when it was formed in 1956. In collaboration with similar representation by the U. S. Navy Bureau of Ships, the U. S. Coast Guard, the principal aluminum alloy manufacturers, a naval architect's office, and a major shipbuilder, after lengthy deliberation, including careful consideration of the international aspects, the Panel succeeded in establishing and publishing a *Tentative Code for the Selection of Wrought Aluminum Alloys for Ship Structures*. This tentative code, supported by the alloy producers and other members of the panel, was an attempt to bring order out of chaos and to serve as a guide for representatives from all branches of the shipbuilding industry.

With the development of the magnesium aluminum alloys, successfully welded strength connections were now a reality. However, owing to differences of opinion as to the actual design values which could be associated with the welds, particularly for the higher tempers, and to the lack of guiding information on this subject, the need for additional reliable information on weld strengths was felt to be apparent; also, it was considered a natural sequel to

64

the information contained in the aforementioned tentative code. To that end, an extensive weld test program was established, and to satisfy this need for information, the Bureau, collaborating with the Society's S-11 Panel, undertook to carry out a major portion of this program in its Metallurgical and Testing Laboratory.

Evidence of the Bureau's continued policy of cooperating to the fullest in approving the light alloys for marine application is best illustrated by the ever-increasing list of American Bureau Classed vessels, registered in the United States and abroad, on which aluminum alloys have been used in various locations and to various extents. These applications have involved principally deck houses and their decks, either in part or in their entirety, although other applications, such as hatch covers, have been in evidence. Special mention should also be made of the two specially designed chemical barges which were built to American Bureau Class in 1961, and which are entirely of welded aluminum alloy construction; also, the Maritime Administration's specially designed hydrofoil vessel on which the Bureau served in a consulting capacity should be mentioned. This hydrofoil is largely constructed of high strength aluminum alloy and is expected to be the highest speed vessel afloat.

The year 1962 will see another large transatlantic passenger vessel which will carry upwards of 2,000 tons of light alloy in its upper structure. The Bureau was involved here in approving the use of one of the weldable aluminum magnesium alloys of French manufacture. This upper structure on the *France* will represent the largest all welded aluminum house structure on an American Bureau Classed vessel, if not the largest on any vessel in the world.

Although it is premature to predict the degree to which these light alloys may penetrate the shipbuilding field as a principal material of construction, research work is on the increase, and the American Bureau is continually active in this type of work in its attempt to provide owners, designers, and builders with the latest information on new developments as a necessary counterpart to information gained wholly from experience.

Development of the Machinery Rules

When the American Bureau of Shipping was incorporated in 1862 as the American Shipmasters' Association, marine engineering was indeed in its infancy, for the greater part of the work at sea was still being done under sail. This is understandable in view of the fact that the speed of the best clipper ships of those days was greater than that of any of the steamships.

66

After Robert Fulton, in 1807, inaugurated the first commercially successful use of steam propulsion with his *Clermont* on the run between New York and Albany, this type of propulsion spread rather rapidly to various rivers. The *Savannah,* in 1819, was the first steamer to make an ocean voyage from America to Europe, although the machinery was operated only part time. It was not until the advent of compound steam engines and surface condensers, with the resultant reduction of coal consumption from about 4 pounds per indicated horsepower per hour to less than 2 pounds, that the steamship was able to compete successfully with the sailing cargo ship.

It is also noteworthy that in 1879 the steamship *Columbia,* which was being built to Class under our survey, was destined to make history as having the first commercial installation of incandescent electric lights. A report of that time states: "The first electric plant that was ever put into operation in the hands of strangers was on the steamship *Columbia* and was installed under directions from Mr. Edison."

The *Columbia* was built by Roach & Son at Chester, Pa., for the Oregon Railroad and Navigation Company. The ship was wired for 115 electric lights in the passenger staterooms and saloons during the summer of 1879, and, in February, 1880, was brought to New York to be fitted out for her voyage around Cape Horn and to have the generating plant installed.

There were three separately-excited 100-volt constant potential dynamos, each capable of supplying 60 lamps of 16 candlepower. The generators were constructed in the laboratory of Thomas A. Edison at Menlo Park, N.J. They were belt-driven and connected in parallel; a fourth dynamo, driven at half speed, was used as their exciter. The generators were connected to a switchboard in the engine room. There were seven feeders of No. 11 B.W.G. copper wire supplying various portions of the accommodations and No. 20 wire was employed for the branch conductors. The conductors were insulated by a paraffined double cotton covering, oiled and painted; those of one polarity were white and those of the other red. Each feeder circuit was

67

controllable at the switchboard, and a switch provided with a key-hole and lock was placed outside each stateroom. The lamp inside was thus controllable by the steward. For safety, one single-pole fusible lead wire was placed in each dynamo circuit, and each individual lamp was provided with a single-pole safety-catch consisting of a small lead wire surrounded by a glass tube about an inch long. In chandeliers, one similar safety-fuse for all the lamps was placed at the top.

The lamps used were evacuated all-glass chambers enclosing carbon filaments. The first ones had horse-shoe shaped paper carbon filaments and frosted globes to soften the light. During the time occupied by the trip around the Horn, Edison made the first bamboo carbon filaments, and sent a supply of the improved lamps across the continent to meet the ship at Portland, Oregon. In a letter to Mr. Edison, dated February 24, 1882, Mr. John Henderson, the advising engineer of the Oregon Railroad and Navigation Company, stated that since the arrival of the ship on the Pacific, they had received a full supply of new bamboo carbon lamps and he quotes Chief Engineer Van Duzer as saying: "I have now 115 lamps in circuit, and have up-to-date run 415 hours and 45 minutes without one lamp giving out."

The plant remained in service for more than fifteen years with no repairs to the machines, except the rewinding of one field coil and a few minor repairs to the bearings.

The second ship built to our Class which had incandescent electric lights was the *Queen Of The Pacific*. She was built by Cramp & Sons at Philadelphia, Pa., for the Pacific Coast Steamship Company and was delivered in May, 1882. It is reported that this plant was installed as a result of the success of the one on the *Columbia*. During the summer of 1882, several other installations were made, and from that time on the use of incandescent lights on merchant ships spread rapidly.

Our first "Rules for the Installation of Electric Lighting and Power Apparatus on Shipboard" were published in the *Record of American and Foreign*

68

Shipping for 1891. The first paragraph of these "Rules" is interesting because it states a philosophy regarding the promulgation of Classification "Rules" which the Bureau still believes to be prudent:

> "Commercial experience with electric lighting on shipboard for over ten years justifies the conclusion that under proper safeguards and with proper care it is the safest method of lighting that has yet been introduced. The Association has therefore adopted the following rules for its installation and regulation."

Also in 1891, our first "Rules for the Construction, Survey and Classification of Machinery and Boilers for Steam Vessels" were published in the same volume of the "Record." From the very beginning the "Rules" had required that every vessel be provided with a good windlass or capstan, of sufficient size to hoist the anchor easily, and that every vessel should also have at least two good and reliable pumps. But it was not until 1876 that the installation of propelling machinery began to be reflected in the "Rules." In that year, requirements were included for shaft tunnels in iron ships. In 1884 requirements concerning floor plates for steamships were included, and in 1888 not only were there requirements for engine and boiler foundations and for coal bunkers, but steam driven windlasses and pumps were also required on all steamships and on all iron or steel sailing vessels of a thousand tons and above. Then in 1891, as just mentioned, separate sections were included in the "Rules" to cover machinery, boilers and electrical installations. In 1904 a section was added for cargo refrigerating apparatus.

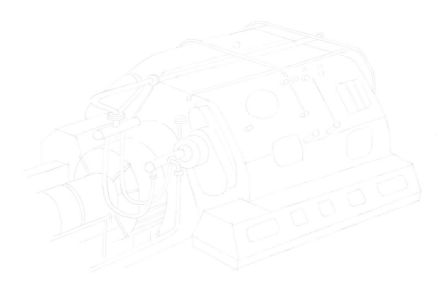

Steam Turbines

By 1917 the machinery plant of most merchant ships consisted of Scotch boilers and steam reciprocating engines. Electricity was used only for lighting and miscellaneous motor driven units. Most of the auxiliaries were either driven off the main engine, or were of the independently driven steam type. Refrigerating machinery was of the ammonia, dry air, or carbon dioxide type. All of this was reflected in the Bureau's "Rules" at that time. There were, to be sure, a few watertube boiler and turbine installations, but these were confined for the most part to the higher powered vessels. Some ships had also been fitted to burn oil in the boilers rather than coal. Diesel engines were in their infancy and the Bureau's first requirements for internal com-

70

bustion engines were included in this edition of the "Rules." Also in the 1917 edition of the "Rules," the Bureau's electrical requirements were coordinated for the first time with those of the American Institute of Electrical Engineers in order to expedite the war effort.

When the wartime program of the Emergency Fleet Corporation was developed, it became evident that there was not sufficient manufacturing capacity in the country to supply Scotch boilers and steam reciprocating engines for all the transports and cargo ships that were contemplated. Accordingly, it was decided to adapt the facilities of the great commercial companies to the construction of double-reduction geared-turbines and watertube boilers. This shift away from the conventional Scotch boiler and steam reciprocating engine was dramatic; for example, out of about 4,800 boilers supplied for the program, 54 percent were of the watertube type and only 46 percent were Scotch boilers. This vast program gave the Bureau a rare opportunity to participate in the development of both geared-turbines and watertube boilers. There were troubles and many breakdowns, particularly with the gears. Thorough systems of survey and inspection, however, were instituted which gradually diagnosed the various troubles so that by 1918 the difficulties had been largely overcome.

A large number of these ships were in active service for many years. In the early 1930's some American operators decided to increase the speed of their turbine driven "Hog Island" type ships in order to qualify for higher mail subsidies. This change in rating, particularly of the turbines and gears, received very thorough study by the members of the Machinery Technical Staff of the Bureau, and eventually led to a simplified method for checking the design strength of turbine rotors. These formulas were first incorporated in the "Rules" in 1936 and, probably because of the American preference for turbine drives, the Bureau was for many years the only Classification Society which published "Rules" covering the basic strength requirements for this type of machinery.

71

Electrical Installations

During the 1920's, two new types of propelling machinery were being developed for use in merchant ships. One of these was the Diesel engine and the other was electric drive for obtaining lower propeller speeds without the use of reduction gears. It is of interest to note that one of the earlier installations combined the use of Diesel engines with direct current generators in series with one direct current propulsion motor, a type of installation which is still quite popular. Later during the twenties, the U.S. Shipping Board undertook a propulsion machinery conversion program of some of the wartime built ships to encourage the development of a variety of Diesel installations. Most were direct connected but several utilized electric drive.

Another system of electric drive was also being developed at this time. This type utilized steam turbines, alternating current generators, and synchronous motors rather than alternating current induction motors as had been previously used by the Navy. A number of fine passenger ships and tankers with this type of drive were built to Class and, as is well known, this was also the type of drive used for over 500 of the T-2 type tankers which were built to Bureau Class during the Second World War.

The advent of the Diesel engine and electric drive for main propulsion machinery opened up much wider use for electricity at sea. The use of electrically-driven auxiliaries with Diesel propulsion seems obvious, but many of the original installations retained steam driven standbys. The electrically-driven auxiliaries, however, proved so successful, that it is now standard even on steamships.

It has long been the practice of the Bureau to maintain close cooperation with the great engineering societies not exclusively concerned with shipping. Active participation by members of our technical staff on committees of these technical societies keeps the Bureau informed of progress in other fields and is most valuable in maintaining the Bureau's engineering and material re-

72

quirements in close accord with existing up-to-date commercial practices.

In 1898, the American Institute of Electrical Engineers (AIEE) recognizing the importance of standardization in the development of electrical engineering, organized a Committee on Standardization. As the industry grew and developed, this committee was also expanded and its work divided among a number of sections. In 1913 an AIEE Marine Committee was organized which developed their Standard No. 45 *Recommended Practice for Electrical Installations on Shipboard.* These first recommendations covered two important divisions, fire protection and marine electrical construction, and it was these which were adopted by the Bureau in 1917 in order to expedite the war effort.

At the time of the great expansion in the size of electric plants aboard ship, the Bureau was represented on the Committee and Standard No. 45 was considerably amplified in 1920, 1927 and subsequent editions. The recommendations give very valuable guidance for the construction and installation of electrical equipment, but, in order to be of maximum benefit to the industry, they have not been framed as minimum standards for the use of regulatory authorities. In order to give guidance to the Bureau's staff in the preparation of our electrical rules, a much smaller group was organized as the Bureau's Special Sub-Committee-Electrical Engineering. Most of its members have also been members of the AIEE Marine Transportation Committee. This close cooperation has worked out extremely well over the years.

Primarily as a result of this arrangement, A. R. Gatewood, Principal Engineer Surveyor at that time, was selected by the Shipbuilders' Council of America to serve as the electrical, as well as the engineering advisor, to the United States delegation at the 1948 Safety of Life at Sea Conference. Because there had been a number of disastrous fires on passenger ships since the 1929 Conference, and because it was felt that by this time at least all first class passenger liners should be provided with emergency generator sets, the American delegation pressed strongly for some basic electrical regulations

73

and was successful in having them included in the Convention. It was felt that no detailed electrical regulations should be included in the Convention. Therefore, the Engineering Committee at the Conference recommended that the Marine Committee of the International Electrotechnical Commission (I.E.C.) be reactivated to draw up recommendations on an international basis which, while not being agreed upon on the diplomatic level, could still be used for guidance, if desired, by Administrations.

In the United States the AIEE Marine Committee was selected to act as the advisory group to the U.S. National Committee, and the Bureau has had representation on I.E.C. Technical Committee 18 since that time. After the formation of the International Standardization Organization (ISO) by the United Nations, the I.E.C. became affiliated with that organization for the preparation of international electrical standards. Technical Committee No. 18 prepared I.E.C. Publication No. 92, *Recommendations for Electrical Installations in Ships*. This document has not only been considered in preparing the Bureau's "Electrical Rules" but has also proved to be of considerable benefit to us in connection with ships being built to our Classification throughout the world.

At the 1960 Safety of Life at Sea Conference, Mr. John W. Heck, our present Chief Surveyor for Machinery, was requested by the U.S. Coast Guard to serve as spokesman for the United States on the Engineering Committee. It is noteworthy that in the 1960 Convention, the electrical regulations have been extended to cover cargo vessels as well as passenger ships.

74

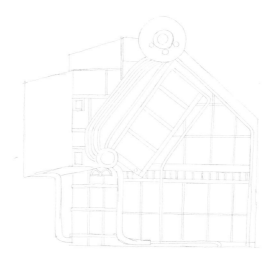

Welded Boilers

Another major advance in the development of machinery plants for merchant ships took place in the early 1930's when the American Bureau approved the general use of electric welding for the fabrication of various major machinery components. The first step had been taken in the late twenties when the main propulsion motor spiders for a number of the turbo-electric drive passenger liners were fabricated by the use of electric arc welding. The difficulty in riveting thicker boiler drum plates, however, was retarding a desired increase in steam pressures. The Babcock and Wilcox Company had done considerable pioneering in development of the use of welding for fabricating watertube boiler drums as well as in the use of x-rays for examining the completed welds. The U.S. Navy had also carried out extensive and thorough investigations of this process. The Navy accepted the use of welded boiler construction as standard in 1931, and about six months later, this process was also accepted by the American Bureau of Shipping and the U.S. Bureau of Marine Inspection and Navigation, now a part of the U.S. Coast Guard.

75

It is of interest to note that at that time the "Rules" for marine boilers used a factor of safety somewhat less than that used in the Boiler Code of the American Society of Mechanical Engineers (ASME), and that all of the boilers built for the Maritime Commission, including its wartime program, were constructed in accordance with Bureau "Rules." The eminently successful operation of these boilers no doubt played a part in the adoption, after the war, of a lower factor of safety by the ASME Boiler Code Committee. This action made it possible for the Bureau to bring its "Rules" into agreement with those of the ASME Boiler and Pressure Vessel Code. At about this time, the ASME Boiler and Pressure Vessel Committee organized a Marine Conference Group as an integral part of its organization, and a member of the Bureau's staff was also elected to membership on the main committee. In order to further this close liaison, the boiler manufacturers are represented on the Bureau's Engineering Committee by the chairman of the ASME Boiler and Pressure Vessel Committee.

More recently, when the ASME set up a separate group to represent the United States in the work of developing an International Boiler Code under ISO auspices, Mr. Gatewood was chosen as one of the American Delegates. Although the work of this committee is not directly applicable to marine boilers, all of the leading boiler manufacturers are represented on ISO Technical Committee No. 11. These organizations supply a very large percentage of the world's marine boilers. ISO/TC11 is the international code making, or standardizing body, but Commission No. XI of the International Institute of Welding (IIW) also concerns itself with boilers, pressure vessels and pipelines. The work of this Commission consists primarily of studies and discussions leading toward the development of new ideas and concepts for advancement of the art. The Bureau maintains a close relationship with the IIW through its American Council and since 1956 Mr. Gatewood has served as the United States Delegate on IIW Commission XI.

Influence of Second World War Experiences

When the United States entered the Second World War, it was of course necessary for the Bureau to increase its staff sufficiently to handle the enormous shipbuilding program. Because of the urgency of the situation, many innovations and improvisations had to be made. One of the earliest of these was in connection with the large number of sabotaged ships which had been interned in various American ports. The crews had deliberately damaged the boilers, crankshafts, connecting rods, engine bed plates and, in fact, all of the machinery installations. It was found possible to repair most of the damage by the use of welding, not only metal arc but also thermit and gas welding. Much of this experience, together with that obtained by the Navy in making emergency repairs during the war, eventually led to the publication by the Bureau of a pamphlet entitled *Procedure for Repairing Cracked Steel Shafts by Welding*.

One of the innovations which was destined to play a continuing role after the war was standardizing on the use of "Freon" as a refrigerant both for ships' stores and for refrigerated cargos, some of the latter consisting of medical supplies which had to be held below certain critical temperatures. Prior to this time, ammonia and carbon dioxide had been the standard refrigerants used in the merchant marine so that the change to "Freon" necessitated the complete revision of the Bureau's refrigeration "Rules." In order to take advantage of the shoreside experience in the use of this new refriger-

77

ant, the Bureau, in cooperation with the American Society of Refrigerating Engineers, prepared a document entitled *Recommended Practice for Mechanical Refrigeration Installations on Shipboard.* This document eventually became American Standards Association Standard No. B59 and forms the basis for the American Bureau's cargo refrigeration requirements. During the war this type of fluoro-carbon refrigerant was available only in the United States, but its use on shipboard has now become universally accepted.

In contrast to the turbines and watertube boilers which were used during the First World War, steam reciprocating engines with watertube boilers were installed in the more than 2700 Liberty ships built to Class during the Second World War. All steam turbine production capacity was being utilized by the Navy and for the higher speed ships, but there were still a number of companies manufacturing machinery which had equipment that could be used for building this type of reciprocating engine. The engine was an early British design, and was chosen because some were already under construction in the United States for the British, and no critical materials were required. On the other hand, there was no longer any capacity in this country for building Scotch boilers, so the type chosen for the Liberty ship program was the cross-drum, sinuous header, watertube boiler. In fact, all of the steamships built to Bureau Class during the war utilized watertube boilers of various types. They were of welded construction and oil fired.

After the war when these ships were being operated by crews of various nationalities, most of whom were not familiar with watertube boilers, the Bureau, at the request of the National Safety Council, of which it has been a member since 1927, organized a small group of experts who prepared a *Safety Manual for Marine Oil Fired, Watertube Boilers.* This manual was very well received and literally thousands of copies were requested. It is hoped that it, at least, helped to reduce the number of boiler casualties which had been occurring primarily as a result of unfamiliarity with the operation of these partially automated, oil fired boilers.

Diesel Engines

Of course, the large manufacturing capacity available for the production of Diesel engines was also utilized in other programs. Some groups of ships were provided with direct drive engines, while others utilized the smaller high speed Diesels in various types of combinations in order to secure the desired horsepower for propulsion. Unfortunately, some rather disastrous crankcase explosions were experienced. Because these casualties were not confined to any one make or type of engine, the Bureau requested a meeting

79

with the engine designers of the companies forming the Diesel Engine Manufacturers' Association, in order to explore the possibility of devising means for alleviating this condition. It was the feeling of this group that the fitting of some form of explosion relief valve or door held the most promise and, accordingly, experiments were carried out both by the Nordberg Company and the Navy in order to develop the necessary basic parameters for devices of this type. The requirement for the fitting of such devices was incorporated in the Bureau's "Rules" in 1948, and our subsequent experience has not only been excellent, but it is gratifying to note that it is now universal practice by all of the manufacturers of marine Diesel engines to fit explosion relief devices.

Following the war, many advances have been made in marine propulsion machinery. Not only have new types been developed, such as the gas turbine and nuclear reactors, but considerable advances have also been made with geared steam turbines and Diesel engines. In order to supply the demand for increased powers for dry cargo ships, as well as for the ever larger tankers and bulk carriers, the builders of the direct drive Diesels have developed their engines until they are now capable of supplying single engines of up to 25,000 horsepower. These engines also utilize residual oil as fuel. The three-fold increase in power since prewar days has been made possible by the use of various means for supercharging two-cycle engines, and this basic change in design also made it necessary for the Bureau to review its Diesel engine requirements. A small panel of engine designers was formed. They developed the basic concepts for the new crankshaft formula. Their suggestions, together with considerable background information, were reviewed by all of the world's leading Diesel engine designers. The Bureau is most grateful to them for their splendid support of this project, as well as for their constructive comments and the additional information which they made available from their own experience. The new formula was first published in our "Rules" for 1956.

80

High Temperature Steam

The major advance made in steam installations since the war has been primarily due to the substantial increase in steam temperature. At the end of the war, temperatures between 700 and 800 degrees Fahrenheit were not unusual. However, for the planned postwar construction, some designers wanted to increase the temperature to over 1000F. Several central power stations and some of the oil refineries had made successful installations in this temperature range, but these were so few and they were so recent that the necessary safeguards had not yet been included in the ASA Standard B-31, *Code for Pressure Piping*.

81

Because of the importance of this new development, the Bureau organized a panel of those whose knowledge and ability in this field were recognized as outstanding. In order to ensure safety and reliability, it was necessary to consider several concepts new to shipboard installations, these including the use of alloy steels and knowledge of their creep and stress to rupture properties at the elevated temperatures. It was also apparent that the former arbitrary method of increasing pipe wall thickness to take care of expansion stresses and working of the ship would no longer suffice, and that a detailed stress analysis would have to be made for each of the high temperature piping systems. All of these and other essential details were included in a document published by the Bureau in 1950 as *An Interim Guide for the Installation of High Temperature Steam Piping on Ships*. A large number of successful installations have since been made and the necessary detailed requirements have been included in the regular "Rules."

The stress to rupture, and particularly the creep properties of the materials also affect the design of high temperature turbines; therefore, it was necessary to reconsider the basic concepts of the turbine formulas for use at the higher temperatures. It might be noted at this point that the change in the steam turbine rules to provide for the use of materials at the high temperatures made the formulas equally applicable for the high temperature gas turbines which were also being developed at this same time.

Reduction Gears

Another notable change since the war, in connection with steam propulsion, has been the adoption of double-reduction gears in greatly increased powers for a large number of ships built both in Europe and in Japan. Reminiscent of the troubles mentioned earlier in connection with the double-reduction gears installed in American ships during the First World War, some

82

of these installations have also encountered difficulties. Careful rechecks were made of the various designs and thorough investigations were made of the casualties. All of this information was reviewed by the Bureau's Special Gear Panel. The Panel felt that the technology of gear design and manufacture was not only so well covered in the available literature, but was also so well understood by the gear manufacturers that nothing would be gained by attempting to include a multitude of details in the "Rules." Rather, it was their feeling that since probably inexperience and, in some cases, limitations of the gear cutting machinery, were largely responsible for most of the difficulties, the need, from a Classification viewpoint, was the establishment of an overall standard which would have to be met and which would also have to be maintained after the ship was put into operation. The actual pattern of tooth contact, as determined by the use of metallic dyes or copper sulphate, was set up as the basic criterion which would have to be met and recorded during the trial trip. Subsequent periodic checks made in the same manner are then compared in order to indicate whether any change in tooth contact has taken place so that, if necessary, corrective measures can be taken. This method of gear control was first tried out by the Bureau in 1959 and, since it is believed to have proved effective when applied in several cases, consideration is being given to its inclusion in the "Rules" as a requirement for Classification.

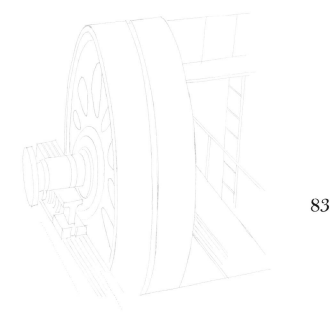

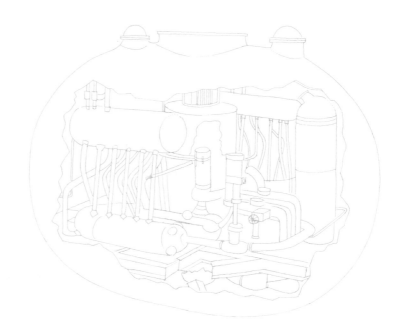

Nuclear Power

Certainly one of the most radical developments in marine engineering has been the advent of nuclear propulsion. The achievement in splitting the atom and in developing the technology, not only to start a chain reaction, but also to control it, has opened up an entirely new source of energy which many feel may eventually prove more economical for marine propulsion than coal or oil.

In January, 1955, the Navy submarine *Nautilus* successfully completed her initial sea trials, being the first ship to utilize nuclear reactors for main propulsion. At the same time, questions began to be raised concerning the adaptation of this new power source for use in merchant ships. Just prior to this time, the Bureau had assigned several members of its technical staff to study this new development, and to consider what impact the application

84

of nuclear propulsion to merchant ships might have on their design, construction, operation and maintenance.

In December, 1954, the Ships' Machinery Committee of The Society of Naval Architects and Marine Engineers' Research Committee organized its Atomic Energy Panel under the chairmanship of Arthur Gatewood, who was then Chief Engineer Surveyor for the Bureau. Later, when the Maritime Administration sent out inquiries concerning a nuclear powered propulsion plant for a merchant ship, the Society, at the request of the Commandant of the Coast Guard, agreed that their Atomic Energy Panel could serve the Coast Guard as an industry advisory panel. Since the membership of the panel included a number who were knowledgeable in the construction and operation of power reactors, as well as representatives from the organizations which were concerned with the building of the *Savannah,* the deliberations of the panel played a most important part in the development of the world's first nuclear merchant ship. The recommendations of the panel were published in 1959 as Society Technical and Research Bulletin No. 3-6 entitled *Safety Considerations Affecting the Design and Installation of Water-Cooled and Water-Moderated Reactors on Merchant Ships.*

The Bureau is also represented on the Special Nuclear Committees of the American Society of Mechanical Engineers' "Boiler and Pressure Vessel Code" and the American Standards Association's "Code for Pressure Piping." As previously mentioned, the Codes of these two great technical organizations have served as the basis for our "Rules" for pressure vessels and piping and, of course, were similarly used in connection with our Classification of the *Savannah.*

The advent of nuclear propulsion brought with it some materials, as well as fabricating and testing techniques, which were new, and since the various components were made in many places, a number of our surveyors have been involved in their construction and testing. Some of the surveyors who supervised the construction of certain important components were also brought to the shipyard to witness their installation and operation on the ship. In this manner the Bureau has developed a group of surveyors whose services can be utilized in the future for carrying out periodic surveys and, also, in connection with new nuclear construction.

When preparations were being made to convene the 1960 Conference on Safety of Life at Sea for the purpose of revising the 1948 SOLAS Convention, it was proposed to include the subject of nuclear ships in the agenda. In organizing the committee to prepare the United States' position on this subject, the Commandant of the Coast Guard, Admiral Alfred C. Richmond, requested the entire Atomic Energy Panel of the Society of Naval Architects and Marine Engineers to serve as a nucleus for the committee under the chairmanship of Arthur R. Gatewood. A number of additional government, industry and labor groups were also invited to nominate representatives to serve on the committee. The Atomic Energy Panel's document was used as the basis for developing the American position paper, and it was also sent to all of the participating Governments as background information.

A fairly large and well diversified group represented the United States at the Conference. Mr. Gatewood was honored by being elected Chairman of the Conference Committee on the Safety of Nuclear Ships, and Captain Murphy, of the Coast Guard, was spokesman for the U.S. delegation. As a result of the deliberations of this committee, the historically important step was taken to include in the 1960 SOLAS Convention a new Chapter VIII, "Nuclear Ships," and a separate Annex "C", which wisely does not form an integral part of the Convention but which does contain a series of recommendations that can be used, if desired, by Administrations as guidance for implementing the regulations.

As demonstrated at the SOLAS Conference, there is considerable interest throughout the world in nuclear propulsion, and prior to the Conference, the Bureau had received several inquiries concerning the application of this type of propulsion to merchant ships. In view of this interest, it was decided

86

in 1959 to organize, as one of the permanent Bureau technical committees, a "Committee on Nuclear Applications". A number of representatives from the leading organizations associated with the development of nuclear power have accepted membership on this committee. Due to lack of experience in operation of nuclear merchant ships, and because the various reactor concepts which are being considered for use will each pose different problems, the Committee has felt that it would be premature at this time to attempt to draw up rules of the conventional type. Instead, the Bureau has followed the practice which it has used on numerous occasions when new developments were being introduced into the marine field, and the Committee has prepared a *Guide for the Classification of Nuclear Ships*. In this way, it is possible to make information available and to discuss the basic considerations for safety and reliability in such a manner that the "Guide" should be of considerable value to designers without tending to hamper the very necessary future developments which will have to be made before this new source of energy can be utilized economically for ship propulsion.

It will have been noted throughout this review of the development of our machinery "Rules" that whenever the Bureau has been faced with new or unusual problems it has, through its own organization of technical committees and panels, sought the best possible advice on the particular problem under consideration, even though this often meant going outside of the marine industry. We would like to take this opportunity to let all of those who have served the Bureau in this capacity know that it has always been a source of great satisfaction to have received such wholehearted support and competent advice from these eminent leaders in their fields. As stated by Mr. J. Lewis Luckenbach, a past President of the American Bureau of Shipping, "The well diversified personnel of these committees insures that the traditional and sometimes very desirable conservatism of a classification society will not preclude the timely application of tested and proven technological innovations as they are developed and approved."

Passenger Liners

During the postwar years, the American Bureau of Shipping has been prominently identified with the building of some of the largest liners in the world. Among these were the *United States,* holder of the mythical Blue Ribbon for the fastest crossing of the North Atlantic. Built by the Newport News Shipbuilding and Dry Dock Company, this vessel is owned by the well known United States Lines Company. In addition, the longest passenger liner in the world, the *France,* built at Saint Nazaire by Chantiers de l'Atlantique for Cie Generale Transatlantique, was constructed to American Bureau of Shipping requirements.

88

In Italy, five large luxury liners were built to American Bureau of Shipping requirements. These included the *Leonardo Da Vinci,* of 33,400 gross tons, the *Cristoforo Colombo,* of 29,200 gross tons, and the *Andrea Doria,* of 29,000 gross tons, constructed by the Genoa plant of Ansaldo S.p.A. Also, the *Augustus,* of 27,000 gross tons, built by Cantieri Riuniti dell'Adriatico at Trieste, and the 27,000 gross ton *Giulio Cesare,* built by the same company at Monfalcone. All five of these liners were ordered by "Italia" Societa per Azioni di Navigazione. Four more liners are now underway, two of 38,000 tons for "Italia" Societa per Azioni di Navigazione and two of 27,000 tons for Lloyd Triestino S.p.A. di Navigazione.

Completed in 1957 to Bureau Class requirements was the A/B Svenska Amerika-Linien transatlantic passenger liner *Gripsholm.* This 23,191 ton vessel was built by Ansaldo S.p.A. at Genoa, Italy.

In 1961, the Home Lines ordered built to Bureau requirements at the Monfalcone, Italy, shipyard of Cantieri Riuniti dell'Adriatico a 30,000 gross ton luxury transatlantic passenger liner.

In addition to the S. S. *United States,* six postwar passenger liners have been finished to Bureau requirements in the United States. These are the American Export Lines *Independence* and *Constitution,* the Moore-McCormack South American vessels *Brasil* and *Argentina,* and the Grace Line luxury liners *Santa Paula* and *Santa Rosa.*

S.S. "America" (*foreground*); S.S. "United States"

S.S. "France"

S.S. "Leonardo da Vinci"

M.S. "Gripsholm"

N.S. "Savannah"

130,000 Deadweight Ton Tankers Being Constructed in Japan

Oil Tankers

The American Bureau of Shipping has been prominently identified with the development of the super size oil tanker, which has taken place since the war. The T-2 tankers of 16,600 deadweight tons, produced in large numbers during the war, are now being rapidly displaced by vessels of 50,000 to 75,000 deadweight tons. The Bureau has been intimately connected with the building of the largest oil tankers in the world, including the 106,000 deadweight ton vessel built at the Bethlehem Steel Company, Quincy, Massachusetts, shipyard for the Manhattan Tanker Company, which is associated with the Stavros S. Niarchos interests, and the two 115,000 deadweight ton tankers built at Kure City, Japan, by the National Bulk Carriers. These latter were the *Universe Apollo* and the *Universe Daphne*. Here, also, were produced seven tankships of 87,000 deadweight tons each, built to American Bureau of Shipping requirements. Even larger tankers are in prospect, and the Bureau has been retained for the Classification of the two 130,000 deadweight ton tankers to be built in Japan for the Japanese oil company Idemitsu

93

Kosan K. K. One of these will be constructed by Ishikawajima-Harima Heavy Industries Company and the other by Sasebo Heavy Industries Company. These huge vessels will be 954 feet 8½ inches long over-all, 141 feet 1 inch in beam, 72 feet 10 inches depth, and of about 73,200 gross tons. Geared-turbine propelling machinery will develop 28,000 shaft horse-power at maximum continuous rating.

Super size oil tankers have been constructed to Bureau Class requirements for the Tidewater Oil Company, Standard Oil Company, (N.J.), Societe Francaise de Transports Petroliers, Cie Maritime des Chargeurs Reunis, Socony Mobil Oil Company, Villain and Fassio E Compagnia Internazionale di Genova, Texaco Inc., Nitto Shosen K. K., Anglo-American Shipping Company (Bermuda), Ltd., an affiliate of Naess Shipping Company, Tokyo Tanker Company, Gulf Oil Corporation, Societa Nazionale Metanodotti, Nereide Societa di Navigazione, Egeria Societa di Navigazione per Azioni, Daido Kaiun K. K., the Stavros G. Livanos interests, the Stavros S. Niarchos interests, the Aristotle S. Onassis interests, Orion Shipping and Trading Company, Carras (U.S.A.), Ltd., Sinclair Refining Company, Standard Oil Company of California, Cities Service Oil Company, Sun Oil Company, Iino Kaiun K. K., Charles Kurz and Company, Caltex (Texaco Inc. and Standard Oil Company of California), Island Navigation Corporation of Tokyo, Union Oil Company of California, Barber Oil Corporation, Atlantic Refining Company, Compagnia Trasporti Petrolio S.p.A.

In addition to their primary activities, the technical staff has been participating in a large and important tanker corrosion control program sponsored by the American Petroleum Institute. The project will study the results of service experience with various corrosion control systems now used in a number of tankers. All of the principal American oil companies are cooperating in the project, and hundreds of cargo tanks will be involved. The corrosion control systems under study include various types of tank coatings, inhibitors, cathodic protection arrangements, and so forth.

94

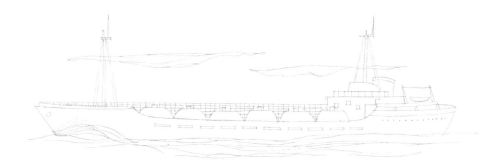

Liquefied Petroleum Gas Carriers

There has been considerable activity in recent years in the development, design, and construction of vessels for the carriage of liquefied petroleum gases at low temperature and for the transportation of special chemical cargos. The development of these new types of vessels involved considerably more investigation by the technical staff than the normal vessel. In the absence of seagoing experience, it was necessary to obtain all available information for the handling of the particular commodity, and to take advantage of all available shore-side experience. The staff has collaborated with the Manufacturing Chemist's Association, the American Petroleum Institute, as well as with regulatory bodies, in the development of vessels for the carriage and handling of special cargos. By participating in such work since immediately after the war, the staff has acquired a broad background of experience with the various factors that have to be considered, over and above the conventional vessel practice, as far as the hull, machinery, electrical, and piping installations are concerned.

95

The Bureau's experience with the carriage of liquefied petroleum gases includes the *Natalie O. Warren*, the first vessel designed solely for the carriage of this cargo, which was put in service in 1947 after conversion from a C-1 type cargo ship. Prior to this time, there had been a few ships fitted with a small number of pressure containers for the carriage of these products. In this connection, many ship designs contemplating low temperatures rather than pressure containers have been considered by the Bureau. Currently there are two ships of different designs building for the transportation of liquefied petroleum gas at atmospheric pressure and low temperature. There is another proposal in which the method of protecting the hull structure from the low temperature differs from the vessels now building, and large scale tests of the insulation and coating combination are in progress.

The experimental and demonstration liquefied methane carrier *Methane Pioneer* has now proven a success, and larger vessels of this type to be built to Bureau requirements are being designed. This was the first ship designed to carry liquefied methane gas at atmospheric pressure and low temperature (−256F). It was converted from a war-built CI-M-AVI type cargo ship by fitting her with insulation within which welded aluminum cargo tanks were placed. Special equipment is required for loading and unloading.

A number of large barges fitted with independent pressure tanks for the transportation of liquefied petroleum gas have been constructed to Bureau Class requirements for use on the Inland Waterways Systems of the United States. In addition, comparatively small self-propelled vessels for this purpose have been constructed to Class. Among these were the *Agipgas Seconda* and the *Agipgas Terza* owned by Agip S.p.A. of Italy; the *Marian P. Billups* and the *Fred H. Billups* built in Holland for Marine Transport Lines.

Another example of the current liquefied petroleum gas carriers is the 32,900 deadweight ton *Esso Puerto Rico* constructed for one of the subsidiaries of the Standard Oil Company, (N.J.), by Cantieri Riuniti dell'Adriatico at Monfalcone. This is a combination vessel, being fitted to carry oil also.

96

Largest of the liquefied petroleum gas carriers will be the 46,100 dead-weight ton vessel now being constructed for General Shipping Company, Tokyo, to Bureau requirements by Mitsui Shipbuilding and Engineering Company. This vessel is designed to carry oil as a combination purpose ship.

Now building to Bureau Class requirements for Bridgestone Liquefied Petroleum Gas Company of Japan is a 20,000 deadweight ton liquefied petroleum gas carrier which will be the first ship of this type utilizing a freezing system for the cargo. It will be constructed by Mitsubishi Nippon Heavy Industries, Yokohama Shipyard and Engine Works.

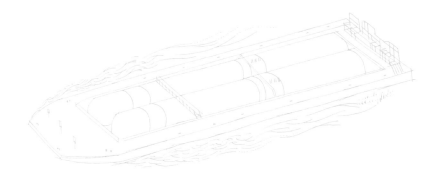

Chemical Carriers

A large number of chemicals have been certified as to safety for carriage on the great rivers of the United States by the United States Coast Guard. Many big barges of special design have been constructed, since the end of the war, for this purpose to Bureau Class requirements. In addition, ocean-going tankships for the transportation of chemicals have been constructed to Class. Among these were the 16,500 deadweight ton *Leland I. Doan* and *Marine Dow-Chem* built for Marine Transport Lines by the Bethlehem Steel Company, Shipbuilding Division.

97

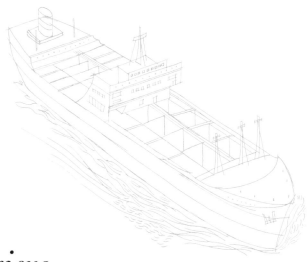

Bulk Carriers

Ocean-going and Great Lakes bulk carriers, designed for the transportation of iron ore, bauxite, gypsum, paper pulp and coal, have been increasing rapidly in size and number. Some of these have been of the self-unloading type. In the latter category, and built to Bureau Class requirements, was the *Kaiser Gypsum,* constructed for the Henry J. Kaiser Company, Oakland, California, by Kure Shipbuilding and Engineering Company, Kure City, Japan. Other vessels of this type, the bauxite carriers *J. Louis* and *Richard,* were built for Universe Tankships, Inc., by the Kure Shipyards Division of the National Bulk Carriers, Kure City, Japan.

Under way in Japan, at present, are four of the largest colliers ever constructed. Building to Bureau Class requirements are two of 44,000 dead-weight tons each, which will be constructed by Kawasaki Dockyard Company, Kobe, Japan, for the Triton Shipping Company. Two of 35,000 dead-weight tons will be constructed for Naess Shipping Company interests by

98

Nippon Kokan K.K., Tsurumi, Japan. These vessels will haul coal from the United States to the steel mills in Japan.

With the completion of the Saint Lawrence Seaway Canal system, which makes it feasible for larger vessels to enter the Great Lakes from the sea, the Bureau has been involved with the construction of the largest vessels now operating on, or to, this fresh water body of lakes. Bulk iron ore carriers have been constructed to Bureau Class of the maximum size that can transit the new locks. These vessels can be 730 feet in length and 75 feet in beam. More recent has been the trend to "jumboize" existing vessels, such as the T-2 type oil tankers, to this maximum size and to convert them to Great Lakes bulk carriers by constructing a new and larger mid-body cargo section, joining this to the existing bow and stern section containing the propelling machinery. In this connection, it might be mentioned that there have been converted recently, or are to be converted, for ocean-going use or use on the Great Lakes, more than fifty ships, and, in addition, about forty have been, or will be, lengthened. In some conversions, only the internal structure and deck are modified, while in others new middlebodies are attached to existing bow and stern sections. These middlebodies have been designed as ocean-going bulk carriers, Great Lakes type bulk carriers, container carriers, LPG carriers, and special chemical carriers.

Among the largest bulk iron ore carriers constructed on the Great Lakes recently to Bureau Class requirements, each over 700 feet in length, are the *Shenango II,* owned by The Shenango Furnace Company, and the *John Sherwin* of the Interlake Steamship Company, both having been constructed at the Toledo, Ohio, yard of the American Ship Building Company. Constructed by the Great Lakes Engineering Works was the *Arthur B. Homer* of the Bethlehem Steel Company. The Manitowoc Shipbuilding, Inc., built the *Edward L. Ryerson* for Inland Steel Company. The latter shipyard also built the big self-unloader bulk carrier *Adam E. Cornelius* for the American Steamship Company.

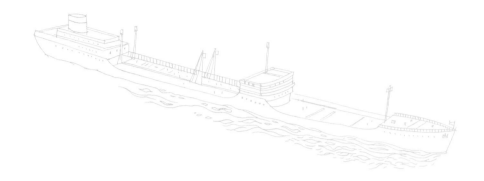

Combination Ore or Oil Carriers

The Bureau was associated with one of the first combination ore or oil carriers to be built. This special type of vessel has, in recent years, been developed in size to match some of the super size oil carriers. Largest of these ore or oil carriers will be the two 67,500 deadweight ton vessels now being constructed in Japan for San Juan Carriers, Ltd., subsidiary of the Utah Construction Company. One each will be built by Nippon Kokan K.K., Tsurumi Yard, and Mitsui Shipbuilding and Engineering Company. Large vessels of this type have also been built to Bureau requirements for Universe Tankships, Inc., subsidiary of the National Bulk Carriers, New York; Oswego Ore Carriers, Ltd., subsidiary of Marine Transport Lines; Olin Mathieson Shipping Corporation; Thomas Entz Tanker G.m.b.H., Hamburg, Germany; States Marine Lines, New York; Triton Shipping Company, New York; and Santa Isabel Compania Naviera S. A., an affiliate of the Orion Shipping and Trading Company, New York.

100

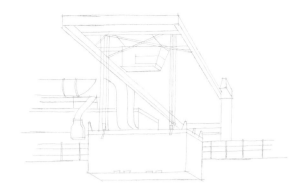

Container Ships

Other postwar developments of some importance were the introduction of roll-on/roll-off ships and container vessels. One of the first of these of large size was the *Carib Queen*. It was converted from a Navy LST. Vehicles were rolled on and off the ship under their own power, with exit and egress points at several locations. Following this, the Bureau Classed the roll-on/roll-off vehicle ship *Comet,* constructed new from special designs for the Military Sea Transportation Service. This was a comparatively large vessel. It has been successfully operated in transoceanic service.

Conversion of existing vessels into cargo container ships has been successfully accomplished by a number of operators. Largest of these were the two Grace Line vessels *Santa Eliana* and *Santa Leonor*. Converted from standard war-built C-2 type cargo ships, the project involved lengthening and widening of the vessels in order to carry a maximum number of large metal cargo container boxes stowed in specially designed guides, or slots, in the enlarged holds. The Bureau was also involved in a similar conversion of five C-2 cargo vessels for the Pan Atlantic Steamship Company. Other lines have partially converted, to Bureau Class requirements, existing vessels to load container boxes. These lines include the Matson Line, Bull Lines, and the United States Lines. A number of the new cargo liners currently being constructed by the subsidized shipping companies of the United States will have special provisions made for the loading and stowing of a limited number of cargo container boxes.

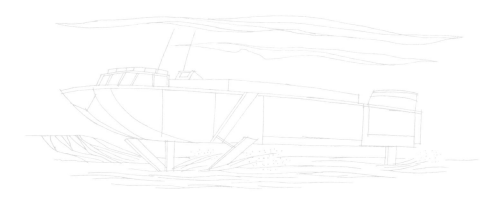

Hydrofoils

The Bureau, in recent years, Classed several hydrofoil vessels which were built overseas. Currently, an experimental 104 foot long hydrofoil vessel with a design speed of 60 knots is building under our survey for the Maritime Administration of the United States. The vessel incorporates many novel machinery features which differ from the other hydrofoil vessels in Class. The main propulsion machinery will be an aircraft type combustion gas turbine which will be modified for marine service. A completely independent propulsion system will be installed for maneuvering in and out of port at low speed. It will consist of a small combustion gas turbine in combination with water jet propulsion, rather than a conventional propeller. Additional hydrofoil vessels are now being built to Bureau Classification requirements in shipyards abroad.

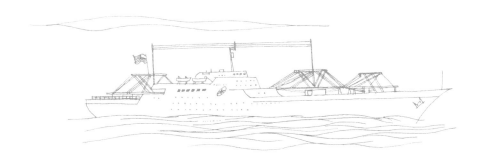

The First Nuclear Powered Commercial Vessel

The first and only nuclear powered commercial vessel in the world, the *Savannah,* has been, since early 1957, an important project in the annals of the American Bureau of Shipping. Built for the Maritime Administration of the United States Department of Commerce by New York Shipbuilding Corporation, Camden, N.J., this combination passenger and cargo liner was completed in 1961 and will be in commercial service in 1962.

Preliminary structural designs for the vessel were reviewed and approved by the Bureau's technical staff before the building contract was placed late in 1957. Long before then members of the technical staff had been conducting intensive studies of nuclear power, and had taken study courses to familiarize themselves with the technical problems involved.

In addition to regular attendance of Bureau surveyors at the shipyard and at sub-contractor's works, specially trained members of the headquarter's staff followed closely all phases of the design, construction and installation of the components relating to the nuclear plant. In addition, specially selected surveyors were assigned to the plants of the manufacturers of these components, and arrangements were made to have the same surveyors in attendance at the shipyard during the installation. By this means, the Bureau developed within its organization a group of surveyors from among whom there will be several who will have well-grounded familiarity with the design, construction, and installation of any part of the power plant, and who may be called upon for service which may be required in the maintenance of the Classification of the ship. These same surveyors are now available for assignments as new nuclear projects develop.

One of the more interesting vessels recently built to Bureau Class is a nuclear ship servicing barge for maintaining and servicing the reactor plant of the N.S. *Savannah*. This non-propelled barge is provided with facilities for storing, shielding, and cooling expended fuel elements and control rods. The barge is also fitted with a system for receiving radio-active waste materials and liquids, and preparing them for disposal.

Services

The primary functions of the American Bureau of Shipping are the establishment of rules for the design, construction and maintenance of ships and their machinery, rules aimed at insuring that these ships will satisfactorily perform the services for which they are intended; and the issuing of certificates and reports attesting to compliance with the "Rules." However, by virtue of the world-wide establishment of surveyors, the specially trained technical staff, and the ability to organize special committees on a strictly impartial basis, some services somewhat beyond the scope of the primary functions are provided to the industry.

There is contained in this part a description of some of the more outstanding of these services.

Load Line, Safety, and Tonnage

The International Safety of Life at Sea Convention of 1929 and The International Load Line Convention of 1930, together constituted a tremendous advance in the establishment of uniform principles and rules for the promotion of safety of life at sea. These two Conventions, along with the Safety of Life at Sea Convention of 1948, the latter superseding the 1929 Convention, provided international standards for safety at sea mutually acceptable to all of the subscribing nations, thereby greatly facilitating the clearance of ships on international voyages.

The obligations for the enforcement of the regulations are well beyond the capacity of the national appropriate enforcing agencies in many of the countries signatory to these conventions. Accordingly, provision was made which would allow the Administration of a signatory nation to grant recognition to an organization, or several organizations, for the carrying out of the surveys and the issuing of certificates on its behalf. Under these provisions, various countries have extended recognition to different organizations in varying degrees, either in whole or in part. The Bureau is proud of the confidence expressed in its organization by the recognition granted to it.

The Bureau has been authorized by the Governments of Belgium, Brasil, Canada, China, Cuba, Denmark, Egypt, France, Greece, Honduras, India, Israel, Korea, Liberia, the Netherlands, Norway, Pakistan, Panama, Philippines, Portugal, the Republic of South Africa, Spain, Sweden, Switzerland, Thailand, Turkey, the United States, and Venezuela to assign load lines and to issue load line certificates for vessels registered under their flags. The Bureau, through its British Technical Committee, is also authorized to issue load line certificates on British flag vessels. There are at present nearly 4,000 vessels, of approximately 27,000,000 gross tons, having valid ocean load line certificates issued by the Bureau. The Bureau is also authorized by Canada and the United States to issue load lines for vessels operated solely on the Great Lakes. Of vessels required to be certified under the Great Lakes Load Line Rules of the two Countries, the Bureau has issued load lines to 450 vessels totaling about 2,389,000 gross tons. In addition, special certificates have been issued for nearly 1,000 river type hopper barges of about 700,000 gross tons for voyages between Chicago and Gary on Lake Michigan.

Brasil, China, Cuba, Egypt, Greece, Liberia, Pakistan, Panama, and Venezuela have authorized the Bureau to carry out surveys on vessels of their registry for the purpose of issuing, on their behalf, certificates as required by the 1948 Safety of Life at Sea Convention. There are in existence nearly 1,000 vessels of about 11,000,000 gross tons which have been issued Safety, Safety Equipment, and Safety Radio-telegraphy certificates by the Bureau as required by that Convention.

Although not as yet on an international basis, every maritime nation requires that ships engaged in international trades be assigned tonnages. The Bureau has been authorized by the Governments of Greece, Liberia, and Panama to measure vessels under their registry, and to issue certificates in accordance with tonnage rules in effect in their respective countries. There are nearly 1,500 vessels totaling about 15,000,000 gross tons for which the Bureau has issued national tonnage certificates.

107

Cargo Gear

In response to a request on the part of the shipping industry in 1951, the Bureau formed a committee to consider, and set forth, standards for the certification of the construction and survey of cargo gear on merchant vessels. This request stemmed from the fact that a number of maritime nations had

108

specific regulations relative to test procedures to be applied to cargo gear before it was put into use, as well as regulations requiring subsequent inspections of the cargo gear, whereas other countries, including the United States of America, had no such requirements. Vessels without proper registers of cargo gear often met with delays in loading or unloading cargo while the cargo gear was being tested and inspected before the vessel could be loaded or unloaded.

The Bureau's Committee is referred to as the Special Subcommittee-Cargo Gear. Its members include shipowners, naval architects, representatives from the U. S. Coast Guard, underwriters, and stevedoring interests.

The first task of the Committee was to review the various existing national laws and recommendations from international bodies in order that a practical and workable set of requirements could be promulgated, regulations which would at the same time be recognized on an international basis. The results of these considerations culminated in the publication entitled, *Requirements for the Certification of the Construction and Survey of Cargo Gear on Merchant Vessels and Code of Recommended Precautions Against Accidents Connected with the Loading and Unloading of Merchant Vessels,* which was issued in 1952. This booklet was in two parts. The first part contained twelve sections under the title of "Cargo Gear" dealing with definitions, design criteria, test procedures for loose gear, wire rope, proof testing of the gear as a unit both in new and existing vessels, periodic surveys, repair and additions to cargo gear, shoreside gear, wire rope and chains, annealing, Register of Cargo Gear and Certificates. The second part of the booklet was devoted to four sections containing recommendations intended to promote safe conditions in which to work while loading and unloading vessels.

The Special Subcommittee-Cargo Gear continues to be active and since the original issue of the cargo gear requirements, revisions were made in 1954, 1958, 1959, 1960, and 1961.

The 1960 revision entailed considerable alteration to the forms of certificates originally issued, and these have now been revised so as to be in substantial agreement with the forms of certificates recommended by the International Labor Office. At the same time, the second part of the cargo gear requirements referring to recommended precautions against accidents was deleted because these matters are now covered by national laws and are no longer needed.

Registers of Cargo Gear, issued by the Bureau since this activity was started, have been recognized by the United States Coast Guard, the agency having jurisdiction over all United States registered vessels. Since the modification in 1960, the United States Department of Labor, having jurisdiction over foreign flag vessels in United States ports, has also granted recognition. In increasing numbers many other countries throughout the world are accepting the Registers as indicating satisfactory compliance with their national regulations.

While the cargo gear surveys are not considered a part of the normal Classification of vessels, the owners of Bureau Classed vessels have availed themselves of this service to the extent that there are more than 800 vessels which maintain American Bureau of Shipping *Cargo Gear Registers.* In association with this work, the Bureau has made every effort to keep the owners of vessels carrying these Registers aware of new governmental regulations on this subject as they come to our attention from time to time.

Twelve years ago cargo gear matters were very unsettled. In addition to the delays to ships not having proper certification, there was an absence of design standards, which was a handicap to a shipyard or contractor furnishing new gear or repairing old gear. Today it is believed the fundamental factors of safety expressed in the Bureau's "Rules", modified from time to time to keep pace with this important subject, will be of help to the maritime industry.

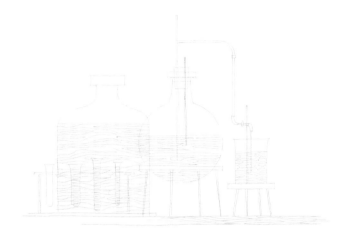

Gas Hazards

THE CERTIFICATION OF GAS CHEMISTS AND STANDARDS FOR THE CONTROL OF GAS HAZARDS ON VESSELS TO BE REPAIRED

The approval of qualified chemists to undertake the issuing of gas chemist certificates to vessels to be repaired which have been carrying or burning combustible or flammable liquids, or carrying flammable compressed gases, has long been one of the services which the Bureau has performed for the industry, although it is not normally considered a part of Classification. These certificates, commonly known as gas free certificates, are referred to in U. S. Coast Guard Regulations and in U. S. Department of Labor Safety and Health Regulations for Ship Repair. The impetus given to this work by the latter's regulations has resulted in many new chemists applying for certification. Our Special Subcommittee-Gas Hazards, which is under joint sponsor-

111

ship with the National Fire Protection Association, completed a revision of the *Standards for the Control of Gas Hazards on Vessels to be Repaired,* which was approved at the annual meeting of that association, May, 1960. These Standards are familiarly known in the marine industry as N.F.P.A. 306.

It will be of interest to note the events leading up to the Bureau's participation in 1922, when certification of gas chemists was first undertaken and later, in 1945, when a Committee under joint sponsorship of the National Fire Protection Association was formed and developed standards which are the basis of those published today.

It is about one hundred years since the first full cargo of petroleum products was transported by sea. This cargo was carried in the brig *Elizabeth Watts,* a vessel of 244 tons, on a voyage from Philadelphia to London in 1861. The cargo was carried in barrels. Subsequent to that date, sailing vessels were carrying oil in tanks built into the ships. But it was not until 1878 that the first tanker, as such, was built to carry oil in bulk using the skin of the ship as the boundary of the cargo spaces.

Literature on the history of tankers intimates that early in the ocean transportation of oil the hazards involved became apparent, and the fundamentals of separating cargo tanks from machinery spaces and living quarters by cofferdams, the proper venting arrangements, and the rule that no open lights be permitted, were deemed essential for the safe operation of the ships. Likewise, the need to gas free the cargo spaces and other areas subject to accumulation of gases, before repairs were commenced, was of prime importance. The old method of sampling the atmosphere of tanks and other spaces was done by such means as a bottle filled with water which was emptied in the presence of the atmosphere to be tested, then corked and removed to a laboratory for testing. Since the laboratory work is done by the chemist to determine whether or not the atmosphere is gas free, it has naturally followed that he also boards the vessel to obtain the sample so that in the end he can certify that a safe condition has been obtained for the work intended

112

to be done. Thus the chemist has long been an important entity in determining that repairs on tankers, as well as other types of vessels that use oil for fuel, can safely be undertaken.

The rather complicated relationship between owners, ship repairers, and underwriters which occurs when vessels are in a shipyard resulted in the early 1920's in a feeling that it would be advantageous to set forth, in writing, an acceptable procedure for handling the gas hazards problem on vessels subject to repair that had carried petroleum products, either as cargo or fuel. The primary result of accidents on vessels that have carried flammable or combustible liquids have been explosions and fires; therefore, it is quite understandable that this matter was dealt with by a marine committee of the National Fire Protection Association, although from the point of view of safety of men, the permissible concentration of vapors is far below the explosive or flammable range. The original standards on this subject were developed in 1922 and published by the National Fire Protection Association as "Appendix A" of the *Regulations Governing Marine Fire Hazards*. "Appendix A" had the following sub-title: "Regulations for Freeing Oil Tanks, Bunkers and Compartments of Dangerous Concentrations of Flammable, Explosive or Toxic Gases Previous to Entering for any Purpose or Making Repairs on Oil Burning or Oil Tank Vessels."

"Appendix A", while only some 1500 words in length, including recommendations for gas freeing of tanks, did a fine job in spelling out the fundamentals in the philosophy of obtaining the condition "safe for men and safe for fire" as indicated by the fact that it was nearly a quarter of a century before it was completely revised.

In 1945, a reorganization of the committee set up dealing with gas hazards on vessels to be repaired took place which resulted in the formation of a joint committee of the American Bureau of Shipping and the National Fire Protection Association. This committee is a sub-group of the Marine Fire Protection Committee of the National Fire Protection Association and de-

113

veloped *Standards for the Control of Gas Hazards on Vessels to be Repaired*, which was first adopted by the National Fire Protection Association in 1947. The Committee has since amended the "Standards" from time to time. It should also be added that the certification of gas chemists was taken over entirely by the American Bureau of Shipping, and this work is done by a Committee Passing on Applicants which is selected from the Members of the Joint Committee.

The present N.F.P.A. 306, while based on the original philosophy of "Appendix A" insofar as the position of the chemist is concerned, has been changed to a considerable degree from the early regulations. These regulations devoted considerable attention to the methods of gas freeing and safety procedures in shipyard operations, such as ventilation, lighting arrangements, and emergency requirements for entering spaces not thoroughly gas free, and these particular thoughts have been deleted from the new "Standards" for the following reasons:

First, the methods of gas freeing are subject to continuous improvement in techniques and, as the important point is satisfying the chemist that a proper condition exists to undertake the work in hand safely, it is hardly worthwhile to include in the regulations subject matter that becomes antiquated with advances in the art.

Secondly, safety procedures or practices in the shipyard are, under normal circumstances, items outside of the activity of the gas chemist whose job is the determination that a safe condition exists on the vessel. Therefore the new "Standards" omitted any details on general shipyard safety procedures to be followed.

A consideration of the great number of dry dockings and repairs accomplished day after day to vessels carrying flammable liquids or gases, and using petroleum products as fuel, encouragingly reveals the steady decline in accidents that have been sustained as the years have passed. For this, must go credit to all of the industry.

114

7

Industry Awards and Technical Recognition

Recognition of technical achievements by individuals on the Bureau staff have been marked over a long period of years by many citations and awards. Likewise, a number of the staff have been elected to high office in many technical societies in the United States and abroad.

In this part mention is made of only a portion of this recognition which has been accorded in the more recent years of the life of the Bureau.

Awards

The 1940 "Miller Memorial Medal" of the American Welding Society was awarded in 1941 to David Arnott, at that time Vice President and Chief Surveyor of the Bureau. This medal is presented for conspicuous contributions to the art and sciences of electric welding. Mr. Arnott was again honored when in 1947 he was awarded "The David W. Taylor Medal" by The Society of Naval Architects and Marine Engineers. This was only the ninth award of this much coveted gold medal which is given by the Society in recognition of "notable achievement in Naval Architecture and Marine Engineering." In making the award, the Society stated, "Mr. Arnott's contribution to the art of ship design and construction lies in his rare combination of scientific attainment in the fields of mechanics and materials with his rich experience of the service behavior of ships. He is endowed with that clarity and logic of line which has enabled him to separate the essential truths from the mass of theories and assumptions which surround the mechanics of ship design and from the conflictions of operating data as well." Mr. Arnott reached high office in the Society, serving as a Vice President and Member of Council.

After the end of World War Two, J. Lewis Luckenbach, then President of the Bureau, was awarded the "Distinguished Public Service Award" by the United States Department of the Navy. The citation accompanying the award stated, "For meritorious service during World War Two when the American Bureau of Shipping, under the direction of President J. Lewis Luckenbach, conducted the inspection survey of practically every merchant ship constructed in this country, including those turned over to the Navy Department for service in transporting urgently needed supplies and manpower to the fighting fronts in all countries of the world." During his career with the Bureau, Mr. Luckenbach was honored by being elected President

116

of the Board of Trustees of Webb Institute of Naval Architecture, Glen Cove, Long Island, New York. He was for many years a Vice President of the Society of Naval Architects and Marine Engineers. He served repeatedly as Chairman of the Annual Merchant Marine Conference conducted by The Propeller Club of the United States.

Walter L. Green, while President of the Bureau, was greatly honored when he received from the Society of Naval Architects and Marine Engineers in 1955, "The Vice Admiral 'Jerry' Land Medal." This gold medal is given for "outstanding accomplishment in the marine field" and this was only the fourth time the Society had made this particular award. At the time, Mr. Green had been elected a Vice President and Treasurer of the Society and had been a member since 1918. In 1956, Mr. Green was further honored by the Society when he was elected President for a two year term, becoming the 22nd President of this Society which was formed in 1893.

Mr. Green served a three year term as President of the Welding Research Council of the Engineering Foundation, and for a number of years was President of the Board of Trustees of Webb Institute of Naval Architecture. On June 1, 1958, he received the Honorary Degree of Doctor of Science at the 73rd Annual Commencement Exercises of Wagner College, Staten Island, New York.

David P. Brown, current President of the Bureau, received in 1957, "The David W. Taylor Medal" from the Society of Naval Architects and Marine Engineers. This gold medal was presented to Mr. Brown "for notable achievement in Naval Architecture and in honored recognition of his technical accomplishments, his dynamic leadership and his outstanding contribution to the engineering profession and to the Society." Mr. Brown has been further honored by the Society by being elected in recent years a Vice President and Treasurer.

Mr. Brown is a member of the Board of Trustees and Treasurer of Webb Institute of Naval Architecture. Since 1958 he has been a member of the

117

Welding Research Council of the Engineering Foundation.

He served on the Special Technical Sub-Committee in the preparation of the United States Proposals to the 1929 and 1948 International Safety of Life at Sea Conventions; the Sub-Committee which was appointed under the Board of Investigation originated in 1943 by the Secretary of the Navy to inquire into the Design and Methods of Construction of Welded Steel Merchant Vessels; and the Working Sub-Committee of the Ship Structure Committee which is now continuing the work of this Board under the direction of the Secretary of the Treasury. Since 1947 he has served as a member of the Ship Structure Committee.

Arthur R. Gatewood, Vice President—Engineering, has been honored by many technical engineering societies, both in the United States and abroad, and maintains membership in the principal organizations.

He is a Vice President and Member of Council of The Society of Naval Architects and Marine Engineers, New York, and is Chairman of the Atomic Energy Panel of the Technical and Research Committees of the Society. As a member of The Institute of Marine Engineers, London, he is Vice President for the United States and is a Member of Council. He is a Fellow of the American Institute of Electrical Engineers. Long active in the American Society of Mechanical Engineers, he now serves on its Boiler and Pressure Vessel Committee. In 1948, he served as an advisor and was spokesman on the Engineering Committee for the United States delegation to the Safety of Life at Sea Conference held in London. At the more recent Conference in 1960, he served as Chairman of the Conference Committee on the Safety of Nuclear Powered Ships.

In 1943, during the vast Liberty shipbuilding program when 2,700 vessels of this type were constructed, the Bureau was singularly honored by the United States Government when the names of two of its past presidents were chosen to be the cognomens for two Liberty ships constructed at the great plant of the Bethlehem Fairfield Shipyard, Baltimore, Md. On May

118

11th of that year, the S.S. *Stevenson Taylor* was launched, being sponsored by Mrs. G. Campbell Taylor, wife of the late Commander Taylor's grandson. Stevenson Taylor was President of the American Bureau of Shipping from 1916 to 1926.

On May 12th the S.S. *Charles A. McAllister* was launched, being christened by Mrs. Charles A. McAllister, widow of the late Captain McAllister. Captain McAllister joined the Bureau as Vice President in 1919, and in 1926 was elected President, serving until his death in 1932. Captain McAllister earned his title in the U. S. Coast Guard, serving from 1892 until 1919. During the last fourteen years of his connection with the Coast Guard, Captain McAllister had the title of Engineer-in-Chief.

APPENDIX

PUBLICATIONS

OF THE AMERICAN BUREAU OF SHIPPING

Record of the American Bureau of Shipping—yearly ship register.

Rules for Building and Classing Steel Vessels—yearly.

Rules for Building and Classing Vessels—Wood Vessels.

Rules for the Construction of Steel Cargo Barges.

Rules for the Construction of Steel Tank Barges.

Rules for the Construction of Self-Propelled River Vessels.

Requirements for the Certification of the Construction and Survey of Cargo Gear on Merchant Vessels.

Guidance Manual for making Manganese Bronze Propeller Repairs.

Guidance Manual for Loading T-2 Tankers.

The Bulletin—monthly.

Members of the American Bureau of Shipping
1962

DAVID A. ARNOTT . . New York, N.Y.
MUNGER T. BALL . . Port Arthur, Texas
OWEN E. BARKER . . . New York, N.Y.
HANS G. BAUER . . . . Trenton, N.J.
PURCELL T. BAUMGARTNER
                    New Orleans, La.
FRED A. BILLHARDT . . New York, N.Y.
FLOYD H. BLASKE . . Jeffersonville, Ind.
WILLIAM E. BLEWETT, Jr.
                    Newport News, Va.
BENJAMIN M. BLOOMFIELD
                    Houston, Texas
ALFRED BLUM . Jackson Heights, N.Y.
FRANK N. BOWERS . . New York, N.Y.
RALPH L. BOYER . Mount Vernon, Ohio
DAVID P. BROWN . . . New York, N.Y.
TROY H. BROWNING. . . Detroit, Mich.
JAMES H. BULL . . . . . Avondale, La.
E. D. BUTCHER . . . . Houston, Texas
JOHN T. BYRNE. . . . New York, N.Y.
GEORGE W. CALLAHAN Cleveland, Ohio
IRA A. CAMPBELL . . . New York, N.Y.
BRAXTON B. CARR . Washington, D.C.
JOHN M. CARRAS . . . New York, N.Y.
RALPH E. CASEY . . . New York, N.Y.
RALPH J. CHANDLER . .Los Angeles, Cal.
RALPH C. CHRISTENSEN New York, N.Y.
PERCY CHUBB 2nd . . New York, N.Y.
JOHN CLARK . . . . .New Orleans, La.
GRANVILLE CONWAY . New York, N.Y.
ADAM E. CORNELIUS, JR.. Buffalo, N.Y.
CLIFFORD G. CORNWELL New York, N.Y.
JAMES G. CRAIG . . Long Beach, Cal.
MORRIS CREDITOR. . . Cincinnati, Ohio
JEROME B. CROWLEY Pompano Beach, Fla.
WENDELL N. DAMONTE. New York, N.Y.

JACK R. DANT . . . San Francisco, Cal.
WILLIAM S. DAVIDSON, JR.
                    New York, N.Y.
WALTER F. DILLINGHAM
                    Honolulu, Hawaii
GARRETT S. DITMARS San Francisco, Cal.
VERNE N. DREW . . . New York, N.Y.
ROBERT G. DUNLOP . . Philadelphia, Pa.
ROBERT R. DWELLY . .New York, N.Y.
HARRY B. DYER . . . Nashville, Tenn.
HERBERT F. EGGERT. . New York, N.Y.
GLEN V. EVANS. . . . Cleveland, Ohio
PHILIP V. EVERETT . . New York, N.Y.
JAMES A. FARRELL, JR. . New York, N.Y.
JESSE P. FEICK . . . . Sheboygan, Wis.
MILTON F. FILLIUS, JR. San Diego, Cal.
EDWARD J. FLYNN. . . . . Mobile, Ala.
LAWRENCE C. FORD . San Francisco, Cal.
JOHN M. FRANKLIN . . New York, N.Y.
ROBERT E. FRIEND . . Milwaukee, Wis.
JAMES C. FRINK. . . . New York, N.Y.
FRED B. GALBREATH San Francisco, Cal.
MILLARD G. GAMBLE . New York, N.Y.
ARTHUR R. GATEWOOD New York, N.Y.
WALTER R. GHERARDI. New York, N.Y.
C. DAVID GIBBONS . . New York, N.Y.
JOHN T. GILBRIDE. . . New York, N.Y.
CONSTANTINE P. GOULANDRIS
                    New York, N.Y.
ROBERT L. GRAY . . . . Ashland, Ky.
WALTER L. GREEN . . Stamford, Conn.
WILLIAM PURNELL HALL Baltimore, Md.
CHARLES HASKILL . River Rouge, Mich.
JOHN I. HAY. . . . . . Chicago, Ill.
RAYMOND M. HICKS. . New York, N.Y.
LEWIS C. HOST . . . . New York, N.Y.

124

JOHN M. B. HOWARD .	New York, N.Y.
RICHARD E. HOWE . .	New York, N.Y.
THOMAS E. HUGHES . .	.La Grange, Ill.
E. N. W. HUNTER . . .	Portland, Ore.
GENE C. HUTCHINSON .	Cleveland, Ohio
THOMAS C. INGERSOLL	
	San Francisco, Cal.
GEORGE INSELMAN . . .	New York, N.Y.
HAROLD JACKSON . . .	New York, N.Y.
WILLIAM E. JACOBSEN	Schenectady, N.Y.
ELMER L. JEFFERSON . .	New York, N.Y.
ALFRED P. JOBSON . . .	New York, N.Y.
WILLARD F. JONES . . .	New York, N.Y.
ROBERT J. JURGEN . .	New York, N.Y.
CLETUS KEATING . . .	New York, N.Y.
HARRY X. KELLY . .	New Orleans, La.
RICHMOND K. KELLY .	Maplewood, N.J.
JOHN E. KENNEY . . .	New York, N.Y.
CHARLES R. KHOURY .	Cleveland, Ohio
ALBERT E. KIHN . .	San Francisco, Cal.
GEORGE KILLION . .	San Francisco, Cal.
EMIL A. KRATOVIL . .	New York, N.Y.
CHARLES KURZ	Philadelphia, Pa.
EMORY S. LAND . .	Washington, D.C.
MONRO B. LANIER . .	Pascagoula, Miss.
LEWIS A. LAPHAM . . .	New York, N.Y.
COSTAS M. LEMOS . . .	New York, N.Y.
HAROLD C. LENFEST .	New York, N.Y.
HENRY J. LESTER . . .	Cleveland, Ohio
A. R. LINTNER	Seattle, Wash.
STAVROS G. LIVANOS .	New York, N.Y.
SIDNEY LIVINGSTON .	San Francisco, Cal.
EDGAR F. LUCKENBACH, JR.	
	New York, N.Y.
DANIEL K. LUDWIG . .	New York, N.Y.
JOSEPH T. LYKES	Tampa, Fla.
EDWARD G. MADDOCK	New York, N.Y.
J. V. C. MALCOLMSON .	New York, N.Y.
WALTER E. MALONEY .	New York, N.Y.
J. ARTHUR MARQUETTE .	Boston, Mass.
CLARENCE D. MARTIN, JR.	
	Washington, D.C.
WALTER L. MARTIGNONI	
	San Francisco, Cal.
ROBERT W. MARVIN .	Pittsburgh, Pa.
FREDERICK J. MAYO .	Pascagoula, Miss.
JOHN A. McCONE .	Washington, D.C.
EMMET J. McCORMACK .	New York, N.Y.
H. W. McCURDY	Seattle, Wash.
T. R. McLAGAN	Montreal, Que.
JAMES K. McLEAN	Mobile, Ala.
WILFRED J. McNEIL . .	New York, N.Y.
F. A. MECHLING	Joliet, Ill.
STANLEY A. MIDNIGHT .	Cleveland, Ohio
W. W. MITCHELL . .	Los Angeles, Cal.
KURT MOLTER	New York, N.Y.
WILLIAM T. MOORE . .	New York, N.Y.
EDMOND J. MORAN . .	New York, N.Y.
CLARENCE G. MORSE .	San Francisco, Cal.
ROBERT H. MORSE, JR. . .	Chicago, Ill.
N. HERBERT MULLEM .	New York, N.Y.
ALBERT G. MUMMA . . .	Harrison, N.J.
ERLING D. NAESS . . .	New York, N.Y.
GEORGE W. NEARE . .	Cincinnati, Ohio
ANDREW NEILSON . . .	New York, N.Y.
JOHN R. NEWELL	Bath, Me.
STAVROS S. NIARCHOS .	New York, N.Y.
M. NIELSEN	New York, N.Y.
LOUIS W. NIGGEMAN	San Francisco, Cal.
NORMAN B. OBBARD .	Pittsburgh, Pa.
RILEY O'BRIEN	Chicago, Ill.
ARISTOTLE S. ONASSIS .	New York, N.Y.
GILBERT B. OXFORD . . .	Boston, Mass.
AUSTIN J. PADDOCK . .	Pittsburgh, Pa.
DANIEL L. PARRY . . .	New York, N.Y.
ARTHUR R. PARSONS . .	St. Louis, Mo.
GEORGE A. PETERKIN, JR.	
	Houston, Texas
JOHN G. PEW, JR..	Chester, Pa.
HARRY W. PIERCE	Camden, N.J.

125

HERMAN T. POTT . . . . St. Louis, Mo.
DARRELL L. POVEY . . Los Angeles, Cal.
WILLIAM B. RAND . . . New York, N.Y.
WILLIAM F. RAPPRICH . Cleveland, Ohio
WALTER W. REED . . . New York, N.Y.
JOHN D. REILLY . . . New York, N.Y.
JOHN D. REILLY, JR. . . New York, N.Y.
NICHOLAS B. RETHYMNIS New York, N.Y.
ALFRED C. RICHMOND Washington, D.C.
TORKILD RIEBER . . . New York, N.Y.
JAMES C. RIEGER . . . Cleveland, Ohio
PETER J. RILEY . . . Cleveland, Ohio
JOHN D. ROGERS . . . . Houston, Tex.
WILLIAM C. RYAN . . . Los Angeles, Cal.
LEIGH R. SANFORD . . New York, N.Y.
ARTHUR J. SANTRY, JR. New York, N.Y.
HARRY G. SCHAD . . . Philadelphia, Pa.
H. RIPLEY SCHEMM . . . Detroit, Mich.
CHARLES F. SCOTT . . New York, N.Y.
WILLIAM H. C. SEELIG . New York, N.Y.
RANDOLPH SEVIER . . San Francisco, Cal.
HERBERT L. SEWARD

     Old Saybrook, Conn.
STUART W. SEXSMITH . Cleveland, Ohio
E. J. SHEARER . . . . . London, Eng.
WILLIAM A. SHEEHAN . New York, N.Y.
HALERT C. SHEPHEARD

      Washington, D.C.
FRANK P. SILLIMAN . . Pittsburgh, Pa.
D. E. SKINNER . . . . . Seattle, Wash.
JOHN E. SLATER . . . New York, N.Y.
HERRIOT SMALL . . . San Francisco, Cal.
J. BARSTOW SMULL . . New York, N.Y.
LYNDON SPENCER . . . Cleveland, Ohio
THOMAS E. STAKEM . Washington, D.C.
HENRY G. STEINBRENNER Cleveland, Ohio

EDWIN L. STEWART . . Scarsdale, N.Y.
DANIEL D. STROHMEIER New York, N.Y.
LOUIS P. STRUBLE, JR. . Pittsburgh, Pa.
VICTOR J. SUDMAN . . New York, N.Y.
ARTHUR C. SULLIVAN, JR. . Chicago, Ill.
DALE E. TAYLOR . . . New York, N.Y.
GEORGE C. TAYLOR . . . St. Louis, Mo.
EDWARD L. TEALE, JR. . . Camden, N.J.
MICHAEL K. TEWKSBURY

     Fort Lauderdale, Fla.
A. M. THOMPSON . . . . Chicago, Ill.
PAUL L. TIETJEN . . . Pittsburgh, Pa.
A. K. TOBIN . . . Honolulu, Hawaii
J. HERBERT TODD . . . New York, N.Y.
M. SPALDING TOON . . . Pittsburgh, Pa.
THOMAS M. TORREY . . New York, N.Y.
E. STORM TROSDAL, JR. . Savannah, Ga.
SOLON B. TURMAN . New Orleans, La.
LAURENCE C. TURNER . Cleveland, Ohio
DAVID E. WALLACE No. Vancouver, B.C.
C. RUSSELL WALTON . . . Boston, Mass.
DONALD WATSON . . San Francisco, Cal.
JOHN L. WELLER . . . Edgewater, N.J.
R. D. WEST . . . . . Manitowoc, Wis.
FRED R. WHITE, JR. . . Cleveland, Ohio
H. LEE WHITE . . . . New York, N.Y.
HAROLD M. WICK . . . New York, N.Y.
JOHN M. WILL . . . . New York, N.Y.
SOREN WILLESEN . . . . Boston, Mass.
PARKER S. WISE . . . New York, N.Y.
J. C. WOELFEL . . . . Long Beach, Cal.
JOHN B. WOODWARD, JR.

     Newport News, Va.
DAVID A. WRIGHT . . New York, N.Y.
MILES F. YORK . . . New York, N.Y.
ROBERT G. ZENER . . . Seattle, Wash.

126

OFFICERS AND COMMITTEES
of the American Bureau of Shipping
1962

DAVID P. BROWN, *President*

LEWIS C. HOST, *Senior Vice President*

KURT MOLTER, *Treasurer*

DANIEL L. PARRY, *Secretary*

ARTHUR R. GATEWOOD, *Vice President—
Engineering*

N. HERBERT MULLEM, *Assistant Treasurer*

WILLIAM H. C. SEELIG, *Assistant Secretary*

WALTER L. GREEN, *Honorary Vice President* HAROLD M. WICK, *Assistant Vice President*

BOARD OF MANAGERS

Term Expires January, 1962	*Term Expires January, 1963*	*Term Expires January, 1964*
JAMES A. FARRELL, JR.	GEORGE W. CALLAHAN	WILLIAM E. BLEWETT, JR.
JOHN M. FRANKLIN	JACK R. DANT	WALTER R. GHERARDI
GENE C. HUTCHINSON	ROBERT G. DUNLOP	JOHN M. B. HOWARD
HAROLD JACKSON	PHILIP V. EVERETT	HARRY X. KELLY
WILLARD F. JONES	RICHMOND K. KELLY	GEORGE KILLION
CLETUS KEATING	CHARLES R. KHOURY	DANIEL K. LUDWIG
CHARLES KURZ	MONRO B. LANIER	JOSEPH T. LYKES
EDWARD G. MADDOCK	J. ARTHUR MARQUETTE	CLARENCE G. MORSE
JOHN D. REILLY	EMMET J. McCORMACK	ANDREW NEILSON
DANIEL D. STROHMEIER	JOHN D. ROGERS	LEIGH R. SANFORD
	JOHN M. WILL	HARRY G. SCHAD
	MILES F. YORK	RANDOLPH SEVIER

CLARENCE D. MARTIN, JR.
Under Secretary of Commerce for
Transportation

ADMIRAL ALFRED C. RICHMOND
Commandant, United States
Coast Guard

THOMAS E. STAKEM
Chairman, Federal Maritime Commission

COUNSEL

CLETUS KEATING

STANDING AND FINANCE COMMITTEE

JAMES A. FARRELL, JR.   ANDREW NEILSON   DANIEL D. STROHMEIER
RICHMOND K. KELLY   MILES F. YORK

CLASSIFICATION COMMITTEE

WENDELL N. DAMONTE   WILLIAM T. MOORE   DANIEL D. STROHMEIER
JOHN T. GILBRIDE   ANDREW NEILSON   JOHN M. WILL
HAROLD JACKSON   †ADMIRAL A. C. RICHMOND   MILES F. YORK

And 4 members appointed monthly from the Membership to serve for two successive
   meetings.

THE TECHNICAL COMMITTEE

PAUL E. ATKINSON   ‡RADM. RALPH K. JAMES   HERBERT L. SEWARD
RICHARD B. COUCH   WILLIAM B. JUPP   RADM. H. C. SHEPHEARD,
WILLIAM J. DORMAN   MERRILL E. KINGSBURY   (Ret.)
ELMER A. GEARY   JOHN B. LETHERBURY   †RADM. IRVIN J. STEPHENS
WILLIAM F. GIBBS   ARTHUR M. LISSENDEN   EDWIN L. STEWART
LESTER M. GOLDSMITH   DOUGLAS C. MACMILLAN   ROBERT TATE
JAMES J. HENRY   FREDERICK I. OWEN   EDWARD L. TEALE
‡CHARLES E. HOCH   HAROLD F. ROBINSON   LANGDON H. WALLING
°LUDWIG C. HOFFMANN   ROYDEN H. ROGERS   GEORGE WEIR
DONALD A. HOLDEN   C. RICHARD SCHAEFFNER EDGERTON B. WILLIAMS
JAMES B. HUNTER   MAURICE L. SELLERS   CHARLES ZEIEN

COMMITTEE ON NAVAL ARCHITECTURE

GORDON W. COLBERG   ‡HUBERT KEMPEL   CARL H. SJOSTROM
ALVIN E. COX   ‡CAPT. RICHARDS T. MILLER W. ARNOLD STEWART
ROBERT T. CUNNINGHAM †CAPT. CHARLES P. MURPHY ROBERT J. TAPSCOTT
HOLLINSHEAD DE LUCE   FRANK L. PAVLIK   KENT C. THORNTON
MATTHEW G. FORREST   °VITO L. RUSSO   MERVILLE WILLIS
FRANCIS J. JOYCE

°Maritime Administration.
†United States Coast Guard.
‡National Military Establishment.

128

COMMITTEE ON ENGINEERING

WALTER C. BACHMAN
H. W. BARTH
HANS G. BAUER
JOHN M. DEMPSEY, JR.
WILLIAM ELMER, JR.
ROSS L. FRYER
ROBERT P. GIBLON

HARRISON R. GLENNON, JR.
WILLIAM E. JACOBSEN
†CAPT. ARTHUR W. JOHN-
    SEN
JOHN R. KANE
PAUL J. LOUZECKY
EUGENE PANAGOPULOS
DAVID MYLREA

HAROLD W. SEMAR
RAYMOND C. SHOOK
°EARL S. SHULTERS
CORBEN C. SHUTE
HOWARD M. VARIAN
‡CAPT. W. E. WEISERT
EUGENE P. WORTHEN

COMMITTEE ON NUCLEAR APPLICATIONS

JOHN M. DEMPSEY, JR.
JAMES P. DOYLE
WILLIAM ELMER, JR.
RICHARD P. GODWIN

A. DUDLEY HAFF
MARK L. IRELAND, JR.
ANDREW R. JONES
HARBOROUGH I. LILL, JR.

DOUGLAS C. MACMILLAN
DONALD W. MONTGOMERY
R. T. PENNINGTON

GREAT LAKES TECHNICAL COMMITTEE

HOWARD C. BRAUN, JR.
FRED GREGORY
DAVID A. GROH
MERRILL E. KINGSBURY
CHARLES S. MAIER

†CAPT. JAMES MCINTOSH
GILBERT F. RANKIN
PETER J. RILEY
HENRY G. STEINBRENNER
ABRAHAM S. THAELER

J. PAUL THOMPSON
HOWARD M. VARIAN
EDGERTON B. WILLIAMS
WILLIAM E. ZIMMIE
ARTHUR J. ZUEHLKE

WESTERN RIVERS TECHNICAL COMMITTEE

WESLEY J. BARTA
WILEY L. BYERS, JR.
DAVID R. DELAY
ROBERT L. GRAY
GEORGE L. GRUNTHANER

GEORGE P. HOGG
CLARENCE R. HORTON, JR.
R. W. KRIEGER
JOHN W. OEHLER

ARTHUR R. PARSONS
JAMES F. ROGAN
JOHN F. SEEMANN
BOYCE WILLIAMSON
WILLIAM H. SWIGGART

BELGIAN TECHNICAL COMMITTEE

HENRI BERSOUX
GASTON BERTRAND
CAMILLE BONNAMI

J. CLAES
PIERRE DE BLICK
GEORGES DE WINNE
GEORGES DUFOUR

FRANK A. VAN DYCKE
ALBERT H. VANDEGHEN
CH. VANDERPERRE

°Maritime Administration.
†United States Coast Guard.
‡National Military Establishment.

129

BRITISH TECHNICAL COMMITTEE

FRENCH TECHNICAL COMMITTEE

ITALIAN TECHNICAL COMMITTEE

NETHERLANDS TECHNICAL COMMITTEE

SPECIAL SUB-COMMITTEE—ELECTRICAL ENGINEERING

SPECIAL SUB-COMMITTEE—WELDING

Ralph D. Bradway
Roger W. Clark
Dr. G. E. Claussen
August Clemens, Jr.

Francis V. Daly
‡Thomas J. Griffin
LaMotte Grover

Allen G. Hogaboom
Arthur A. Holzbaur
†Capt. George C. Steinman

SPECIAL SUB-COMMITTEE—MATERIALS

M. W. Acker
Francis B. Foley
Dr. Maxwell Gensamer
Jesse C. Jones

John R. LeCron
Norman L. Mochel
Richard A. Pomfret

T. T. Watson
R. D. Webb
Dr. A. B. Wilder

SPECIAL SUB-COMMITTEE—GAS HAZARDS

Joint Committee of the American Bureau of Shipping and the National Fire Protection Association.

Braxton B. Carr
Henry A. Gilbert
†Capt. Samuel G. Guill
Samuel H. Harrison
William B. Jupp
Joseph J. LaRocca

Joseph B. Meyer
Rex V. Phelps
Dr. H. G. Schneider
RAdm. H. C. Shepheard,
  (Ret.)

John M. Techton
J. Paul Thompson
Charles J. Tiedemann
T. T. Wilkinson
J. Lyell Wilson

SPECIAL SUB-COMMITTEE—CARGO GEAR

Edwin E. Benzenberg
°Francis G. Ebel
†Capt. Samuel G. Guill
Donald F. MacNaught

Joseph W. McDiarmid
Roscoe Meadows, Jr.
Ralph W. Netterstrom
Louis B. Pate
Robert F. Rader

RAdm. H. C. Shepheard,
  (Ret.)
J. Paul Thompson
Douglas E. Yates

°Maritime Administration.
†United States Coast Guard.
‡National Military Establishment.

131

GREAT LAKES COMMITTEE

George W. Callahan
Adam E. Cornelius, Jr.
Robert R. Dwelly
Glen V. Evans
Jesse P. Feick
Charles Haskill
Gene C. Hutchinson

Charles R. Khoury
Henry J. Lester
Stanley A. Midnight
Riley O'Brien
William F. Rapprich
Walter W. Reed

James C. Rieger
Peter J. Riley
Stuart W. Sexsmith
Arthur C. Sullivan, Jr.
R. D. West
Fred R. White, Jr.

PACIFIC COAST COMMITTEE

Ralph J. Chandler
James G. Craig
Jack R. Dant
Garrett S. Ditmars
Milton F. Fillius, Jr.
Lawrence C. Ford
Fred B. Galbreath
E. N. W. Hunter
Thomas C. Ingersoll

George Killion
A. R. Lintner
Sidney Livingston
Walter Martignoni
John A. McCone
H. W. McCurdy
W. W. Mitchell
Clarence G. Morse
Louis W. Niggeman

Darrell L. Povey
William C. Ryan
Randolph Sevier
D. E. Skinner
Herriot Small
Donald Watson
J. C. Woelfel
Robert G. Zener

WESTERN RIVERS COMMITTEE

Purcell T. Baumgartner
Floyd H. Blaske
E. D. Butcher
Braxton B. Carr
Morris Creditor
Harry B. Dyer
Robert L. Gray

John I. Hay
Robert W. Marvin
F. A. Mechling
George W. Neare
Herman T. Pott
Frank P. Silliman

Louis P. Struble, Jr.
George C. Taylor
A. M. Thompson
Paul L. Tietjen
M. Spalding Toon
David A. Wright

132

Designed, printed and bound in the United States of America
at The Lakeside Press, R. R. Donnelley & Sons Company
Chicago, Illinois and Crawfordsville, Indiana